TEST IT
FIX IT

PRE-INTERMEDIATE

DON'T JUST TEST IT, FIX IT!

English **Verbs and Tenses**

Kenna Bourke

OXFORD
UNIVERSITY PRESS

OXFORD
UNIVERSITY PRESS

Great Clarendon Street, Oxford OX2 6DP

Oxford University Press is a department of the University of Oxford.
It furthers the University's objective of excellence in research,
scholarship, and education by publishing worldwide in

Oxford New York

Auckland Bangkok Buenos Aires Cape Town Chennai
Dar es Salaam Delhi Hong Kong Istanbul Karachi Kolkata
Kuala Lumpur Madrid Melbourne Mexico City Mumbai Nairobi
São Paulo Shanghai Taipei Tokyo Toronto

Oxford and Oxford English are registered trade marks of
Oxford University Press in the UK and in certain other countries

© Kenna Bourke 2003

The moral rights of the author have been asserted

Database right Oxford University Press (maker)

First published 2003
Third impression 2003

ISBN 0 19 438073 4

Illustrated by Tamsin Cook

Text layout and design by
Cambridge Publishing Management Ltd

Printed in China

Contents

How to use *Test it, Fix it*

Test it, Fix it is a series of books designed to help you identify any problems you may have in English, and to fix the problems. Each *Test it, Fix it* book has twenty tests which concentrate on mistakes commonly made by learners.

Test it, Fix it has an unusual format. You start at the **first** page of each unit, then go to the **third** page, then to the **second** page. Here's how it works:

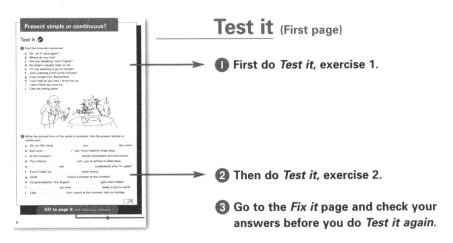

Test it (First page)

➊ First do *Test it*, exercise 1.

➋ Then do *Test it*, exercise 2.

➌ Go to the *Fix it* page and check your answers before you do *Test it again*.

Fix it (Third page)

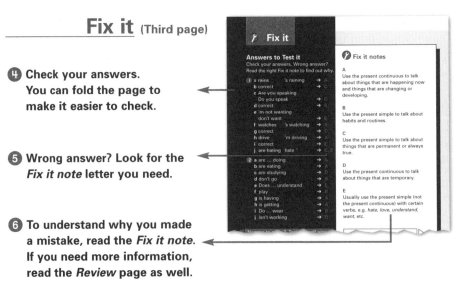

➍ **Check your answers.**
You can fold the page to make it easier to check.

➎ **Wrong answer? Look for the** *Fix it note* **letter you need.**

➏ **To understand why you made a mistake, read the** *Fix it note*. **If you need more information, read the** *Review* **page as well.**

➐ Now go back to the second page and do *Test it again*.

Test it again (Second page)

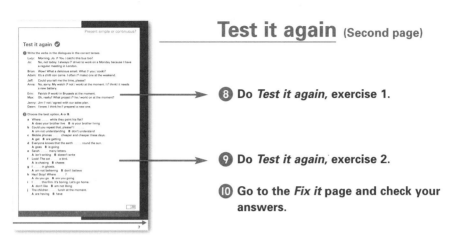

→ ⑧ Do *Test it again*, exercise 1.

→ ⑨ Do *Test it again*,' exercise 2.

⑩ Go to the *Fix it* page and check your answers.

Fix it (Third page)

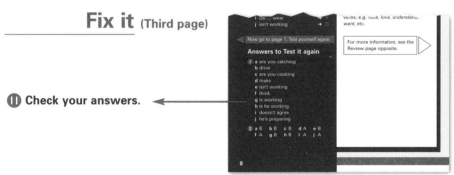

⑪ Check your answers. ◄

Review (Fourth page)

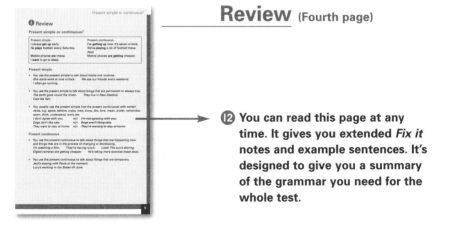

→ ⑫ You can read this page at any time. It gives you extended *Fix it* notes and example sentences. It's designed to give you a summary of the grammar you need for the whole test.

Present simple or continuous?

Test it ✔

1 Find the incorrect sentences.

a Oh, no! It rains again!

b Where do you live?

c Are you speaking much English?

d He doesn't usually listen to me.

e I'm not wanting to go out tonight.

f John watches a film at the moment.

g Yves comes from Switzerland.

h I can't talk to you now. I drive the car.

i I don't think you love me.

j Cats are hating water.

2 Write the correct form of the verbs in brackets. Use the present simple or continuous.

a Oh, no! Bill, what .... you .... (do) now?

b Sam and I .... (eat) more healthily these days.

c This term I .... (study) philosophy and economics.

d The children .... (not / go) to school on Saturdays.

e .... she .... (understand) why I'm upset?

f Every Friday we .... (play) tennis.

g Janet .... (have) a shower at the moment.

h Congratulations! Your English .... (get) much better!

i .... you ever .... (wear) a suit to work?

j Luke .... (not / work) at the moment. He's on holiday.

20

GO to page 8 and check your answers.

Test it again ✔

1 Write the verbs in the dialogues in the correct tenses.

Lucy: Morning, Jo. (a you / catch) this bus too?

Jo: No, not today. I always (b drive) to work on a Monday because I have a regular meeting in London.

Brian: Wow! What a delicious smell. What (c you / cook)?

Adam: It's a chilli con carne. I often (d make) one at the weekend.

Jeff: Could you tell me the time, please?

Anna: No, sorry. My watch (e not / work) at the moment. I (f think) it needs a new battery.

Erin: Patrick (g work) in Brussels for a few weeks.

Max: Oh, really? What project (h he / work) on at the moment?

Jenny: Jim (i not / agree) with our sales plan.

Dawn: I know. I think he (j prepare) a new one.

2 Choose the best option, **A** or **B**.

a Where .... while they paint his flat?
A does your brother live   **B** is your brother living

b Could you repeat that, please? I ....
A am not understanding   **B** don't understand

c Mobile phones .... cheaper and cheaper these days.
A get   **B** are getting

d Everyone knows that the earth .... round the sun.
A goes   **B** is going

e Sarah .... many letters.
A isn't writing   **B** doesn't write

f Look! The cat .... a bird.
A is chasing   **B** chases

g I .... in ghosts.
A am not believing   **B** don't believe

h Hey! Stop! Where .... ?
A do you go   **B** are you going

i I .... this film. It's boring. Let's go home.
A don't like   **B** am not liking

j The children .... lunch at the moment.
A are having   **B** have

20

Fix it

Answers to Test it

Check your answers. Wrong answer?
Read the right Fix it note to find out why.

1
  a ~~rains~~   's raining   → A
  b correct   → C
  c ~~Are you speaking~~
     Do you speak   → C
  d correct   → B
  e ~~'m not wanting~~
     don't want   → E
  f ~~watches~~   's watching → A
  g correct   → C
  h ~~drive~~   'm driving   → A
  i correct   → E
  j ~~are hating~~ hate   → E

2
  a are ... doing   → A
  b are eating   → A
  c am studying   → D
  d don't go   → B
  e Does ... understand → E
  f play   → B
  g is having   → A
  h is getting   → A
  i Do ... wear   → B
  j isn't working   → D

Now go to page 7. Test yourself again.

Answers to Test it again

1
  a Are you catching
  b drive
  c are you cooking
  d make
  e isn't working
  f think
  g is working
  h is he working
  i doesn't agree
  j he's preparing

2 **a** B   **b** B   **c** B   **d** A   **e** B
    f A   **g** B   **h** B   **i** A   **j** A

Fix it notes

A
Use the present continuous to talk about things that are happening now and things that are changing or developing.

B
Use the present simple to talk about habits and routines.

C
Use the present simple to talk about things that are permanent or always true.

D
Use the present continuous to talk about things that are temporary.

E
Usually use the present simple (not the present continuous) with certain verbs, e.g. *hate, love, understand, want,* etc.

For more information, see the Review page opposite.

 Review

Present simple or continuous?

Present simple	Present continuous
I always get up early.	I'm getting up now. It's seven o'clock.
He plays football every Saturday.	We're playing a lot of football these days.
Mobile phones are cheap.	Mobile phones are getting cheaper.
I want to go to sleep.	

Present simple

* You use the present simple to talk about habits and routines.
  She starts work at nine o'clock.   *We see our friends every weekend.*
  I often go running.

* You use the present simple to talk about things that are permanent or always true.
  The moon goes round the earth.   *They live in New Zealand.*
  Cats like fish.

* You usually use the present simple (not the present continuous) with certain verbs, e.g. *agree, believe, enjoy, hate, know, like, love, mean, prefer, remember, seem, think, understand, want,* etc.
  I don't agree with you.   NOT   *I'm not agreeing with you.*
  Dogs don't like cats.   NOT   *Dogs aren't liking cats.*
  They want to stay at home.   NOT   *They're wanting to stay at home.*

Present continuous

* You use the present continuous to talk about things that are happening now and things that are in the process of changing or developing.
  I'm watching a film.   *They're having lunch.*   *Look! The sun's shining.*
  Digital cameras are getting cheaper.   *He's taking more exercise these days.*

* You use the present continuous to talk about things that are temporary.
  Jack's staying with Paula at the moment.
  Lucy's working in the States till June.

Past simple

Test it ✔

1 Find and correct the mistakes.

a Jean-Marie lives in Paris all his life. He died last year.
b I have seen him last Monday.
c The car didn't stopped.
d Did you rang Charlie yesterday?
e I losed my wallet.
f Who did build the Eiffel Tower?
g Look! You droped your keys.
h Where stayed you in Los Angeles?
i Do the children go to school yesterday?
j I didn't saw David. He wasn't there.

2 Write sentences. Use the past simple.

a Mike / not go / to work / last week

....

b Where / you / go / on holiday?

....

c We / stop / the car / to look / at the view

....

d you / see / Natalie / at the party?

....

e Kate / meet / Andy / last year

....

| 15 |

GO to page 12 and check your answers.

Test it again ✅

① Solve the clues to complete the crossword.

Across

1 The children .... all the sweets.

5 Who .... the song called 'My Way'?

7 I .... to call you but you were out.

8 I .... all night but I didn't finish the report.

9 He .... for his burger and left the restaurant.

Down

2 Sarah .... geography and history for twenty years.

3 Peter .... Saskia a long letter.

4 They .... for the bus for an hour but it didn't come.

6 The train .... on time.

8 Phil .... to Bali on business.

② Put the verbs into the story in the correct form.

feel	put	look	run	scream
not believe	blow	say	arrive	not wait

When the Dixons ª .... at their holiday villa, they realized that something was wrong. But what was it? The villa ᵇ .... nice, and the children seemed happy but for some reason they ᶜ .... that the place was dangerous. The villagers ᵈ .... that there were ghosts but the Dixons ᵉ .... in ghosts. They opened the front door and ᶠ .... their cases down. At that moment, a woman ᵍ .... and a cold wind ʰ .... through the house. The Dixons ⁱ .... to find out what or who it was. They turned and ʲ .... back to the car and drove away from the village for ever.

20

⚒ Fix it

Answers to Test it

Check your answers. Wrong answer?
Read the right Fix it note to find out why.

1
	a	~~lives~~	lived	→ A
	b	~~have seen~~	saw	→ A
	c	~~stopped~~	stop	→ B
	d	~~rang~~	ring	→ C
	e	~~losed~~	lost	→ D
	f	~~did build~~	built	→ E
	g	~~droped~~	dropped	→ G
	h	~~stayed you~~	did you stay	→ F
	i	~~Do~~	Did	→ C
	j	~~saw~~	see	→ B

2
a Mike didn't go to work
last week. → B
b Where did you go on
holiday? → F
c We stopped the car to
look at the view. → G
d Did you see Natalie at
the party? → C
e Kate met Andy last year. → D

◀ Now go to page 11. Test yourself again.

Answers to Test it again

1
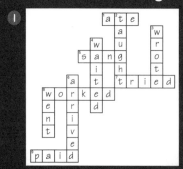

2
a	arrived	f	put
b	looked	g	screamed
c	felt	h	blew
d	said	i	didn't wait
e	didn't believe	j	ran

⚒ Fix it notes

A
Use the past simple to talk about
finished actions in the past.

B
Make the negative form of the past
simple with *didn't* + base form of
the verb.

C
Make past simple *yes/no* questions with
did + subject + base form of the verb.

D
Some common verbs have irregular
past simple forms (see list on page 88).

E
When *who* or *what* are the subject of a
question, don't use *did/didn't* + base
form of the verb.

F
Make past simple questions with a
question word (*what, where, who,
when, how,* etc.) + *did* + subject + base
form of the verb.

G
The spelling changes in some past
simple regular forms.

For more information, see the
Review page opposite. ▷

 Review

Past simple

One of the most common mistakes that people make is to use the present perfect when they should use the past simple, and the past simple when they should use the present perfect. Look at pages 21, 25 and 29 to see what the differences are.

- You use the past simple to talk about finished actions in the past, often with a time expression, e.g. *yesterday, last week, in June, in 2001, five years ago,* etc.
  Jean-Marie lived in Paris all his life.   I saw him last Monday.

- You make the past simple positive form of regular verbs with the base form of the verb + *ed*. The form is the same for all persons.
  I walked.   She walked.   They walked.

- Some common verbs have irregular past simple forms (see list on page 88).
  I lost my wallet.   He went to bed.   They sang 'Happy Birthday'.

Negatives and questions

- You make the negative form of the past simple with *didn't* + base form of the verb. The form is the same for all persons.
  The car didn't stop.   We didn't see him.   They didn't come.

- You make *yes/no* questions in the past simple with *did/didn't* + subject + base form of the verb. The form is the same for all persons.
  Did you ring Charlie yesterday?   Didn't they enjoy the meal?

- When *who* or *what* are the subject of a question, you don't use *did/didn't* + base form of the verb.
  Who built the Eiffel Tower?   NOT   *~~Who did build the Eiffel Tower?~~*

- You make past simple questions with a question word (*what, where, who, when, how*) + *did* + base form of the verb.
  Where did you stay?   NOT   *~~Where stayed you?~~   ~~Where you stayed?~~*

Spelling

- Verbs ending in *e*: add *d*.
  hope   hoped   arrive   arrived
  Verbs ending in *y*: change the *y* to *i* and add *ed*.
  study   studied   cry   cried
  Verbs ending in one vowel + one consonant: double the consonant + *ed*.
  *drop   drop**ped**   stop   stop**ped**   plan   plan**ned***
  Note that if the final syllable of a two-syllable word isn't stressed, you don't double the final consonant.
  open   opened   visit   visited   happen   happened

Past simple or continuous?

Test it ✔

1 Find the correct sentence in each pair.

a Yesterday we walked to the river and back.
b Yesterday we were walking to the river and back.

c I saw Jane while I walked to work.
d I saw Jane while I was walking to work.

e Mark lived in the US for fifteen years.
f Mark was living in the US for fifteen years.

g When did you last see Sam?
h When were you last seeing Sam?

i Judy and Alan met while they worked at Sony.
j Judy and Alan met while they were working at Sony.

2 Six of these sentences are incorrect. Find and correct them.

a When I saw the children, they played a game in the garden.

b At midnight last night, I was lying awake thinking about work.

c Martin didn't read the report when I arrived at the office: he was answering a call.

d When were you arriving last night?

e They were watching TV when the lights went out.

f Pat was writing twenty-two emails yesterday. It took her a long time.

g At two thirty, I was playing squash and Jack was reading a book.

h I didn't talk to Sarah at seven o'clock - I was putting the children to bed.

i It rained when I looked out of the window.

j We took the children to the park yesterday.

15

GO to page 16 and check your answers.

Test it again ✅

1 Choose the best option, **A** or **B**.

a My parents .... hard all their lives.
A were working   **B** worked

b I .... Simon last night. He looked great.
A saw   **B** was seeing

c Mike .... a new job last week.
A was getting   **B** got

d While I .... to the airport, I had a fantastic idea.
A drove   **B** was driving

e Cathy and Nick .... when Jim interrupted.
A chatted   **B** were chatting

f At six o'clock last night I .... in a traffic jam.
A sat   **B** was sitting

g When they got to the park, it ....
A was raining   **B** rained

h When Sammy stopped his bike, he .... off again.
A was falling   **B** fell

i It was a lovely afternoon, so they .... for a walk by the river.
A went   **B** were going

j Luke .... to talk to Jill on his way to work.
A was stopping   **B** stopped

2 Write sentences. Use the past simple and continuous.

a Jackie / spend / all her life / in India

....

b At midnight last night / the wind / blow / and / it / rain

....

c Max / get up / at five / and / work / till / half-past nine

....

d What / you / do / when / I / ring / you?

....

e They / travel / round Africa / when / they / hear / the good news

....

☐ 15

Fix it

Answers to Test it

Check your answers. Wrong answer?
Read the right Fix it note to find out why.

① The correct sentences are:

a → A		**g** → A	
d → D		**j** → D	
e → A			

② **a** ~~played~~   were playing → B, D
b correct   → B
c ~~didn't read~~
   wasn't reading   → B, D
d ~~were you arriving~~
   did you arrive   → A
e correct   → D
f ~~was writing~~
   wrote   → A
g correct   → C, B
h ~~didn't talk~~   wasn't talking → C, B
i ~~rained~~   was raining → B, D
j correct   → A

◁ Now go to page 15. Test yourself again.

Answers to Test it again

① **a** B **b** A **c** B **d** B **e** B
   f B **g** A **h** B **i** A **j** B

② **a** Jackie spent all her life in India.
   b At midnight last night, the wind
      was blowing and it was raining.
   c Max got up at five and worked till
      half-past nine.
   d What were you doing when I rang
      you?
   e They were travelling round Africa
      when they heard the good news.

Fix it notes

A

Use the past simple (not the past
continuous) to talk about finished
actions in the past.

B

Use the past continuous (not the past
simple) to talk about actions in the past
which were not finished.

C

Use the past continuous to describe
actions happening at a particular time
in the past. Also use it to give
background information in stories.

D

Use the past simple and past
continuous together when one action
interrupts another longer action in
the past.

> For more information, see the
> Review page opposite. ▷

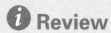 Review

Past simple or continuous?

Past simple	Past continuous
I lived in Belgium when I was a child.	I was living in Belgium when I met James.
It rained all day.	It was raining at ten o'clock.
Frank cooked supper last night.	When Sally got home, Frank was cooking supper.

Past simple

- You use the past simple (not the past continuous) to talk about completed actions in the past.
  It rained all day.   *They bought a CD.*
  (The day is finished.)   (The action is finished.)

- You usually use the past simple (not the past continuous) with certain verbs, e.g. *agree, believe, enjoy, hate, know, like, love, mean, prefer, remember, seem, think, understand, want,* etc.
  I didn't like the hotel.   NOT   ~~*I wasn't liking the hotel.*~~
  She wanted to go.   NOT   ~~*She was wanting to go.*~~
  They understood me.   NOT   ~~*They were understanding me.*~~

Past continuous

- You use the past continuous for unfinished actions in the past, often with a time expression, e.g. *yesterday, at ten o'clock, last year, in June 1999,* etc.
  At 4.30 I was watching a great film on TV.
  (I carried on watching it after 4.30.)
  Mark was living in London in 1999.
  (We know that he continued to live in London after 1999.)

Past simple and continuous

- You often use the past simple and past continuous together. This happens when a long action is interrupted by another shorter action.
  Harry was having a shower when his guests arrived.
  (**1** He was having a shower.   **2** His guests arrived.)
  The phone rang while I was cooking supper.
  (**1** I started cooking supper.   **2** The phone rang.)

- You use the past continuous to describe what was happening at a particular time in the past. This is especially common when you give background information in stories.
  It was snowing and the wind was blowing hard. Suddenly the lights went out.

Test it ✅

1 Find one mistake in each dialogue.

a Bob: I've been to New Zealand last year.
 Jo: I've never been there.

b Sue: Has your brother ever lived abroad?
 Ann: Yes, he's lived in Brussels two years ago.

c Pat: Have you before seen this film?
 Jill: Yes, I saw it last month.

d Mike: Did you meet Patrick before?
 Pete: No, I don't think we've ever met.

e Sam: I've tasted such good coffee never.
 Adam: No, I haven't either. It's lovely.

2 Write the correct form of the verbs in brackets.

Pam: You look well. Have you been on holiday?

David: Yes, I ª... (go) to Cairo two weeks ago.

Pam: What ᵇ... (be) it like? ᶜ... you

.... (have) a good time?

David: Brilliant. In the first week I ᵈ... (visit) the pyramids,

which were amazing. And, guess what? Later that week, I

ᵉ... (ride) a camel! ᶠ... you ever

.... (ride) a camel?

Pam: No, never.

David: I don't recommend it! I ᵍ... never

.... (feel) so uncomfortable in my life.

Pam: ʰ... you .... (take) any photos?

David: Yes, of course! ⁱ... you ever

.... (hear) of the Step pyramid?

I ʲ... (take) some great photos there.

Pam: Yes, I saw a programme about it on TV. Maybe I'll go to Egypt one day.

It sounds fascinating.

| 15 |

GO to page 20 and check your answers.

Test it again

1 **Match the statements.**

a   John never met his father.

b   John has never met his father.

c   My teacher always gave me
    bad marks.

d   My teacher has always given me
    bad marks.

e   I've never been to Peru.

f   I didn't go to Peru.

g   Pat worked for the company for
    thirty years.

h   Pat's worked for the company for
    thirty years.

i   I've written three letters today.

j   I wrote three letters today.

1   It's early afternoon.

2   The speaker is talking about a
    particular holiday.

3   The speaker has left school.

4   It's night-time.

5   The speaker is talking about his/her
    life up to now.

6   Pat doesn't work for the company
    now.

7   John's father is probably dead.

8   Pat still works for the company.

9   The speaker is still at school.

10   John's father is alive.

2 **Choose the best option.**

a   Did you ever hear/Have you ever heard of a game called *Pokémon*?

b   I never went/I've never been to Athens in my life.

c   I never met/I've never met my grandmother. She died before I was born.

d   He never read/He's never read *War and Peace*, but he'd like to.

e   I never saw/I've never seen you before.

f   Did you talk/Have you talked to your boss yesterday?

g   She's never heard/She never heard this song before.

h   Have you seen/Did you see the film on TV last night?

i   I never won/I've never won a prize in my life.

j   Did you ever dream/Have you ever dreamt you could fly?

20

Fix it

Answers to Test it

Check your answers. Wrong answer?
Read the right Fix it note to find out why.

1
a ~~I've been~~ I went → B
b ~~he's lived~~ he lived → B
c ~~Have you before seen~~
  Have you seen ... before → C
d ~~Did you meet~~
  Have you met → A
e ~~I've tasted~~
  I've never tasted → C

2
a went → B
b was → B
c Did ... have → B
d visited → B
e rode → B
f Have ... ridden → A
g 've ... felt → A
h Did ... take → B
i Have ... heard → A
j took → B

Now go to page 19. Test yourself again.

Answers to Test it again

1
a 7 b 10 c 3 d 9 e 5
f 2 g 6 h 8 i 1 j 4

2
a Have you ever heard
b I've never been
c I never met
d He's never read
e I've never seen
f Did you talk
g She's never heard
h Did you see
i I've never won
j Have you ever dreamt

Fix it notes

A
Use the present perfect when it isn't important when you did something. Do not use the present perfect with a past time reference.

B
Use the past simple for completed actions in the past, often with a time reference.

C
The adverbs *ever*, *never* and *before* follow this word order:
Have you ever met Patrick?
No, I've never met him.
No, I haven't met him before.

For more information, see the Review page opposite.

 Review

Present perfect or past simple? (1)
Talking about general experience

The difference between the present perfect and the past simple causes problems for many people. This is perhaps because there are several uses of the present perfect and some of these uses are similar to the use of the past simple. In this book you will find three tests on the present perfect and past simple. Each one deals with a different use of the present perfect. They're organized like this:

Present perfect or past simple? (1) is about using the present perfect for general experience.

Present perfect or past simple? (2) is about using the present perfect for recent events.

Present perfect or past simple? (3) is about using the present perfect for things that are still happening now.

Present perfect	Past simple
I've been to India.	I went to India in 1999.
He's never met Mr Davies.	He didn't meet Mr Davies at the conference.
Have they flown British Airways before?	Did they fly British Airways last month?

- You use the present perfect to talk about your or other people's experiences. The exact time that the experience happened isn't important. Sometimes grammar books call this the 'indefinite past'. You don't usually use a past time reference, e.g. *yesterday, last month, a year ago,* etc., with the present perfect.
  I've seen the Eiffel Tower.   NOT   *I've seen the Eiffel Tower last year.*
  (At some time in my life. It doesn't matter when.)
  John hasn't travelled very much.
  (Never at any time in his life up to now.)

- You use the past simple to talk about completed actions in the past, often with a time reference.
  I saw the Eiffel Tower when I was in Paris last year.
  When he was in America, John didn't travel much. He stayed in New York most of the time.

- You often use the present perfect for experience with these adverbs: *ever, never* and *before*. Note the word order.
  Have you ever met him?   *No, I've never met him.*   *Have we met before?*

- Be careful! The past participles *been* and *gone* have different meanings:
  Tom has been to Hong Kong.   *Tom has gone to Hong Kong.*
  (He went to Hong Kong and now he's back.)   (He's in Hong Kong now.)

Test it ✔

1 Find the correct sentence in each pair.

a When have your friends arrived?
b When did your friends arrive?

c I didn't do the shopping yet.
d I haven't done the shopping yet.

e Have you already had lunch?
f Did you already have lunch?

g The Prime Minister has just landed in Delhi.
h The Prime Minister just landed in Delhi.

i Richard has gone to college last week.
j Richard went to college last week.

2 Find and correct five mistakes in the news reports.

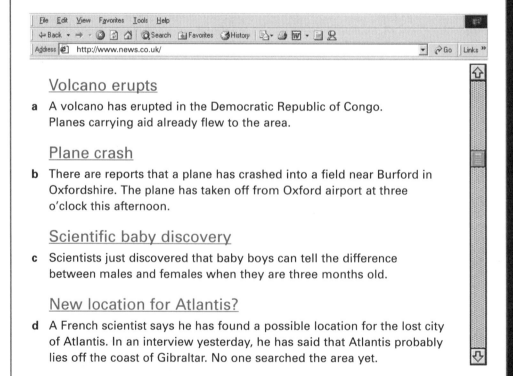

File Edit View Favorites Tools Help

Back ➡ ⊗ ⬚ ⬟ Search Favorites History ⬚ ⬚ ⬚ ⬚ ⬚

Address http://www.news.co.uk/   Go   Links »

Volcano erupts

a A volcano has erupted in the Democratic Republic of Congo.
Planes carrying aid already flew to the area.

Plane crash

b There are reports that a plane has crashed into a field near Burford in
Oxfordshire. The plane has taken off from Oxford airport at three
o'clock this afternoon.

Scientific baby discovery

c Scientists just discovered that baby boys can tell the difference
between males and females when they are three months old.

New location for Atlantis?

d A French scientist says he has found a possible location for the lost city
of Atlantis. In an interview yesterday, he has said that Atlantis probably
lies off the coast of Gibraltar. No one searched the area yet.

10

GO to page 24 and check your answers.

Test it again ✅

1 Choose the best option, **A** or **B**.

a   I'm sorry. The manager ....
    A just left   **B** has just left

b   'Jack, I've found your briefcase.' 'Thanks! Where ....?'
    A have you found it   **B** did you find it

c   Apparently Sarah .... a new job last week.
    A has got   **B** got

d   The dog doesn't need a walk. I .... him out!
    A just took   **B** 've just taken

e   Sam arrived in Peru last night but she .... me yet.
    A hasn't called   **B** didn't call

f   .... the newspaper?
    A Did you already read   **B** Have you already read

g   Scientists .... that there may be life on Venus.
    A just discovered   **B** have just discovered

h   Tom and Louise haven't arrived yet. Their car .... about an hour ago.
    A broke down   **B** has broken down

i   'Jill has found a new boyfriend.' 'Great! Where .... him?'
    A has she met   **B** did she meet

j   Let's not go and see that film. I .... it.
    A 've already seen   **B** already saw

2 Write sentences. Use the present perfect or the past simple.

a   Guess what? You / win / lottery!

    ....

b   Mary / have / a baby / at midnight last night

    ....

c   The President / just / arrive / at Heathrow airport

    ....

d   I / can't believe / you / already / eat / all those sandwiches

    ....

e   Pete / leave / the company / yesterday

    ....

☐ 15

🔧 Fix it

Answers to Test it

Check your answers. Wrong answer?
Read the right Fix it note to find out why.

1 The correct sentences are:

b → F	g → A, D
d → A, B	j → E, F
e → A, C	

2
a ~~already flew~~
  have already flown → A, C
b ~~has taken off~~
  took off → E, F
c ~~just discovered~~
  have just discovered → A, D
d ~~has said~~ said → E, F
  ~~searched~~ has searched → A, B

◀ Now go to page 23. Test yourself again.

Answers to Test it again

1 a B b B c B d B e A
  f B g B h A i B j A

2
a Guess what! You've won the lottery.
b Mary had a baby at midnight last night.
c The President has just arrived at Heathrow airport.
d I can't believe you've already eaten all those sandwiches.
e Pete left the company yesterday.

🔧 Fix it notes

A
Use the present perfect (not the past simple) to talk about recent past events.

B
Use the present perfect with (*not*) *yet* in negative sentences and questions.

C
Use the present perfect with *already* when something has happened sooner than you expected it to.

D
Use the present perfect with *just* to say that something happened very recently; only a few moments ago.

E
Don't use the present perfect with a past time reference. Use the past simple.

F
Use the past simple to talk about completed actions in the past.

> For more information, see the Review page opposite. ▷

 Review

Present perfect or past simple? (2)
Talking about recent events

Present perfect	Past simple
Flight 773 has just landed.	Flight 773 landed at 10.05 this morning.
I've already had lunch.	I had lunch at Guido's yesterday.
Have they spoken to Tim yet?	Did they speak to Tim on Friday?

- You use the present perfect (not the past simple) to talk about things that have or haven't happened in the recent past. This use of the present perfect is common when you give someone news. You use the present perfect rather than the past simple because what you're saying is important now.
  A plane carrying aid has just landed at the airport.
  (Look – there it is on the runway.)
  The bus hasn't arrived yet.
  (It isn't here. I'm waiting for it now.)
  You'll never believe this! I've won the lottery.
  (I'm rich!)

- You use the past simple for finished actions in the past, often with a time expression, e.g. *yesterday, at ten o'clock, last year, in June 1999*, etc.
  The plane landed at six o'clock this morning.
  The bus didn't come until 11.30.
  David won a small prize in the lottery last month.

Just, already and yet

- You often use the present perfect to talk about the recent past with these adverbs: *just, already* and *yet.*
  Use *just* when you mean 'a moment or two ago; very recently'.
  I've just seen Jim.   Have you just let the dog out?
  Use *already* when something has happened sooner than you expected it to.
  Have you already finished work?   Look! I've already read the whole report.
  Use (*not*) *yet* in negatives and questions.
  We haven't seen your new baby yet.   Have you paid the bill yet?

 Note: In American English, it's possible to use either the present perfect or the past simple with *just, already* and *yet*. Both are correct.
I already did the washing-up.   *I've already done it.*
Pete just phoned Sam.   *He's just phoned her.*
Did you invite Carol to the party yet?   *Have you invited her yet?*

Test it ✓

① Which explanation is correct, **A** or **B**?

a I lived in Vienna in 1989.
   A I live in Vienna now.   **B** I live somewhere else now.

b Jane has lived by the sea all her life.
   A She still lives by the sea.   **B** She lives somewhere else now.

c How long have you been a vet?
   A You're still a vet.   **B** You were a vet but now you aren't.

d They studied medicine for eight years.
   A They still study medicine.   **B** They don't study medicine now.

e We have known each other since we were children.
   A We don't know each other now.   **B** We still know each other.

② Find and correct the mistake in each sentence.

a I am here since last week.

b Jules had his new job for a month – he loves it.

c I lived here for ten years but I'm going to move soon.

d David knows Ann for five months.

e I have studied French in 2001.

f How long do you have your motorbike?

g They have known Mark since three days.

h She's had a headache for three o'clock.

i Tony was a teacher for thirty years and he still enjoys it.

j How long are you in this country?

15

GO to page 28 and check your answers.

Test it again ✔

❶ Choose the best option.

a   Jill knows/'s known Philip since they were children.

b   When I was younger, I've been/was a tennis professional.

c   Have/Did you always had that car?

d   They lived/'ve lived in Canada since 1980.

e   Did you study/Have you studied English when you were at school?

f   When did you get/have you got your puppy?

g   I'd/'ve had this computer for many years and it works really well.

h   We lived/'ve lived in this house when I was a child.

i   Jack and Tim have been/were friends since they were at university.

j   Ralph was/'s been in prison since 1998.

❷ Match the speech bubbles.

a   When did you live in Rome?

b   Have you always had a cat?

c   How long were you a teacher?

d   Have you known each other long?

e   Is that your car?

1   About ten years.

2   Yes. I've had it for ages.

3   Yes, I have.

4   In the 1980s.

5   No, we only met a month ago.

15

Fix it

Answers to Test it

Check your answers. Wrong answer?
Read the right Fix it note to find out why.

1 a B → B   d B → B
  b A → A   e B → A
  c A → A

2 a ~~am~~   have been → A
  b ~~had~~   has had → A
  c ~~lived~~   have lived → A
  d ~~knows~~   has known → A
  e ~~have studied~~ studied → B
  f ~~do you have~~
      have you had → A
  g ~~since~~   for → C, E
  h ~~for~~   since → D
  i ~~was~~   has been → A
  j ~~are you~~
      have you been → A

Now go to page 27. Test yourself again.

Answers to Test it again

1 a 's known
  b was
  c Have
  d 've lived
  e Did you study
  f did you get
  g 've had
  h lived
  i have been
  j 's been

2 a 4   b 3   c 1   d 5   e 2

Fix it notes

A
Use the present perfect to talk about an action that began in the past but is still going on now. Don't use the present simple or the past simple.

B
Use the past simple to talk about finished actions in the past.

C
Use *for* to say how long an action has gone on.

D
Use *since* to say when an action started.

E
Don't use *since* to talk about a period of time, e.g. *three days*.

For more information, see the Review page opposite.

 # Review

Present perfect or past simple? (3)
Talking about things still happening now

Present perfect	Past simple
I've been a teacher for five years.	I was a teacher for five years.
Paul hasn't had toothache since he was a child.	He didn't have toothache yesterday.
How long have you had that car?	How long did you have that car?

It can be difficult to decide whether to use the present perfect or the past simple. One way of deciding is to ask yourself if what you're saying is still important now, in the present. Look at the difference between these two sentences:
I had a headache yesterday.
(This is a fact about the past. It's finished. I haven't got a headache now.)
I've had a headache for three hours.
(The headache started in the past but it's important now. My head still hurts.)

- You use the present perfect to talk about unfinished actions that started in the past and still continue now. For actions that are finished, use the past simple.

I've lived here since 1994.	*I lived here in 1994.*
(I still live here.)	(I don't live here now.)
I've had my dog for three years.	*I had a dog for twelve years.*
(I've still got my dog.)	(I haven't got a dog now.)

For and *since*

- You often use *for* and *since* with the present perfect when you're talking about unfinished actions.

- Be careful! You use *for* to talk about the length of time an action has been going on, e.g. *for three years, for two weeks, for an hour, for a year*, etc.
  We've been in France for a week.

- You use *since* to say when the action started: *since 1994, since last week, since I was a child, since five o'clock*, etc.
  We've been in France since Saturday.

- Don't use *since* to talk about the length of time. This is a very common mistake.
  ~~I have had this car since a year.~~
  ~~We've known him since a month.~~

Past perfect or past simple?

Test it ✅

1 Choose the best option.

a When I arrived, the film `already started/had already started`.

b The thief `had gone/went` by the time the police arrived.

c I thought it was the best thing I `ever saw/'d ever seen`.

d When I`'d put/put` the children to bed and tidied up, I watched the news on TV.

e Pam thought she `saw/'d seen` Mike somewhere before.

f We advertised the car but no one `had wanted/wanted` it.

g By the time we got to the vet's, our hamster `died/had died`.

h As I `walked/'d walked` in, he jumped up and shook my hand.

i Steve couldn't get into the house because he`'d lost/lost` his key.

j `Had you already left/Did you already leave` when the fight started?

2 Find the incorrect sentences.

a By 1999, I'd waited five years for an answer.

f James hadn't been there long before the trouble started.

b When Phil got to the shop, it had closed.

g Yesterday I hadn't been to school. I stayed at home.

c I'd broken five glasses yesterday.

h Just as I got there, the class started.

d When I saw Carol ten years later, she changed completely.

i Last week she'd run a marathon.

e The moment I saw you, I knew we met before!

j By the time he'd made his decision, she'd gone.

| 20 |

GO to page 32 and check your answers.

Test it again ✔

❶ Write the correct form of the verbs in brackets. Use the past perfect or past simple.

We ª .... (already / leave) for the airport when Jim
ᵇ .... (say) that he ᶜ .... (forget) his
passport.

This morning Shirley ᵈ..................................... (wake up) late, then she
ᵉ .... (miss) the bus, so by the time she ᶠ ....
(arrive), the lecture ᵍ .... (already / start).

When I ʰ .... (go) back to Egypt ten years later, nothing
ⁱ .... (changed): the Nile ʲ .... (be) still
magical and the people were as welcoming as ever.

Last week John ᵏ .... (find) a bill he ˡ ....
(not / pay). It was strange—he ᵐ .... (never / forget) to pay
bills before.

When Ciaran and Sophie ⁿ .... (meet) for the first time, they
ᵒ .... (not / like) each other but now they're married!

❷ Match the two halves of each sentence.

a	As we stepped on to the plane,	1	Charlie crept downstairs.
b	John wanted to tell us a joke but	2	the engines started.
c	I didn't know	3	she'd broken her leg.
d	When everyone had gone to sleep,	4	you'd bought a new car.
e	Fran couldn't go to school because	5	he'd forgotten it.

☐ 20

Fix it

Answers to Test it

Check your answers. Wrong answer?
Read the right Fix it note to find out why.

1
  a had already started   → A
  b had gone   → A
  c 'd ever seen   → A
  d 'd put   → A
  e 'd seen   → A
  f wanted   → B
  g had died   → A
  h walked   → C
  i 'd lost   → A
  j Had you already left   → A

2
  a correct   → A
  b correct   → A
  c ~~'d broken~~   broke   → B
  d ~~changed~~   'd changed → A
  e ~~met~~   'd met   → A
  f correct   → A
  g ~~hadn't been~~   didn't go   → B
  h correct   → C
  i ~~'d run~~   ran   → B
  j correct   → A

Now go to page 31. Test yourself again.

Answers to Test it again

1
  a had already left
  b said
  c had forgotten
  d woke up
  e missed
  f arrived
  g had already started
  h went
  i had changed
  j was
  k found
  l hadn't paid
  m had never forgotten
  n met
  o didn't like

2 **a** 2   **b** 5   **c** 4   **d** 1   **e** 3

Fix it notes

A
Use the past perfect (not the past simple) for a past action which happened before another past action.

B
Use the past simple to talk about completed actions in the past.

C
Use the past simple when two past actions happened at the same time.

> For more information, see the Review page opposite.

 Review

Past perfect or past simple?

Past perfect	Past simple
I'd forgotten my passport. It was at home.	I forgot my passport. Then I lost my ticket.
They hadn't been to France before.	They didn't go to France last year.
The lesson had already started.	The lesson started at two o'clock.

Past perfect

- You use the past perfect (not the past simple) to make it clear that one past action happened before another past action.
  When I got there, the shop had closed.
  (First the shop closed, then I got there.)
  They'd already left for the airport when John said he'd forgotten his passport.
  (First, John forgot his passport. Second, they left for the airport. Third, John said he'd forgotten his passport.)

  Note: The expression of time changes when you use the past perfect:
  Did you see Jane yesterday?
  Had you seen Jane the day before?
  Where did he go on holiday last year?
  Where had he been on holiday the previous year/the year before?

Past simple

- You use the past simple (not the past perfect) to talk about completed actions in the past.
  Did you lock the back door?   Yes, I did.   I broke five glasses yesterday.

- You use the past simple when two past actions happened at the same time.
  Just as I got there, the class started.
  (I got there and the class started at that moment.)
  As we stepped on to the plane, the engines started.
  (We stepped on to the plane. The engines started at the same moment.)

Test it ✔

1 Correct any past tense mistakes you can see.

a Have you seen Martin yesterday?
b When I reached the station, the bus already left.
c It snows all day. I'm fed up with it.
d John is here since last Wednesday.
e Did you ever go to China?
f At three o'clock last night, the children slept.
g Bill was having a shower when the phone was ringing.
h Fred's not here. He's been to Geneva.
i I wasn't understanding what the teacher said today.
j Oh, no! You just broke my computer!
k When have you stopped drinking coffee?
l 'You looked tired last night.' 'Yes, I had been.'
m Did the rain stop yet?
n They've been knowing each other for a couple of weeks.
o When I got home, Jim is playing the piano and Sam watches TV.

2 Choose the best caption for the cartoon.

Have you been good while I've been out?
Had you been good while I've been out?
Have you been good while I've gone out?

16

GO to page 36 and check your answers.

Test it again ✅

1 **Read the beginning of these two stories. Choose the correct options to fill the gaps.**

It ^a _____ heavily during the night and the grass was damp and cold. But as we ^b _____ out into the cool morning air, I ^c _____ a wave of happiness float across me. The sun was shining and the birds ^d _____. Everything suddenly seemed perfect.

Anthony and I ^e _____ each other very long but here we are on our honeymoon! I ^f _____ believe how lovely the hotel was when we arrived last night. As our taxi pulled up outside the front door, a band ^g _____ playing. We ^h _____ to them when suddenly a huge firework ⁱ _____. I ^j _____ at that moment that Anthony and I would be together forever.

a	**A** rains	**B** had rained	**C** has rained	**D** did rain
b	**A** have walked	**B** are walking	**C** walk	**D** walked
c	**A** felt	**B** was feeling	**C** had felt	**D** have felt
d	**A** sang	**B** have sung	**C** had sung	**D** were singing
e	**A** don't know	**B** didn't know	**C** haven't known	**D** hadn't known
f	**A** can't	**B** don't	**C** couldn't	**D** didn't
g	**A** was starting	**B** started	**C** has started	**D** starts
h	**A** were listening	**B** have listened	**C** listened	**D** had listened
i	**A** was exploding	**B** exploded	**C** had exploded	**D** has exploded
j	**A** know	**B** was knowing	**C** knew	**D** have known

2 **Which explanation is correct, A or B?**

a   In 1998, Bill worked for a computer firm.
   A He still works for them.   **B** He doesn't work for them now.
b   I've made a cake.
   A There's a cake now.   **B** There was a cake but now there isn't.
c   Jack's washed the car.
   A The car is clean now.   **B** Jack's still washing it.
d   Paula has gone to work.
   A She's at work now.   **B** She went to work and now she's back.
e   I never met my uncle.
   A My uncle is alive.   **B** My uncle is dead.

15

Answers to Test it

Check your answers. Wrong answer?
Read the right Fix it note to find out why.

1
a ~~Have you seen~~
  Did you see → A
b ~~already left~~
  had already left → H
c ~~snows~~ 's snowed → E
d ~~is here~~ has been here → F
e ~~Did you ever go~~
  Have you ever been → D
f ~~slept~~ were sleeping → B
g ~~was ringing~~ rang → C
h ~~He's been~~ He's gone → D
i ~~wasn't understanding~~
  didn't understand → G
j ~~just broke~~
  've just broken → E
k ~~have you stopped~~
  did you stop → A
l ~~had been~~ was → A
m ~~Did ... stop~~
  Has ... stopped → E
n ~~been knowing~~
  known → G
o ~~is playing ... watches~~
  was playing ...
  was watching → B

2 Have you been good
while I've been out? → E, D

Now go to page 35. Test yourself again.

Answers to Test it again

1 a B b D c A d D e C
   f C g B h A i B j C

2 a He doesn't work for them now.
   b There's a cake now.
   c The car is clean now.
   d She's at work now.
   e My uncle is dead.

Fix it notes

A
Use the past simple for completed actions in the past.

B
Use the past continuous to talk about past actions which weren't finished at a past time or to describe what was happening at a particular time in the past.

C
Use the past simple and continuous together when one action interrupts another longer action in the past.

D
Use the present perfect when it isn't important when something happened. There is a difference between the participles *been* and *gone*.

E
Use the present perfect to talk about recent past events.

F
Use the present perfect to talk about an action that began in the past but is still going on now.

G
Use the simple form (not the continuous form) with certain verbs, e.g. *know, understand,* etc.

H
Use the past perfect (not the past simple) when one past action happened before another past action.

For more information, see the Review page opposite.

 Review

All past tenses

Past simple and continuous

- You use the past simple for completed actions in the past, often with a time expression, e.g. *yesterday, last week, in 1999, on Wednesday*, etc.
  Did you see Martin yesterday?   *I worked for IBM in the 1990s.*

- You use the past continuous to talk about past actions which weren't finished at a past time or to describe what was happening at a particular time in the past.
  What were you doing yesterday afternoon?
  When we arrived the sun was shining and the birds were singing.

- You use the past simple and past continuous together when one action interrupts another longer action in the past.
  They were watching TV when the electricity went off.

Present perfect

- You use the present perfect when it isn't important when something happened. You often use the adverbs *ever, never* and *before* with the present perfect.
  I've met several famous people.   *Have you ever eaten caviar?*

  Note: There's a difference in meaning between the participles *been* and *gone*.
  Fred has been to Geneva.   *Fred has gone to Geneva.*
  (He went to Geneva and now he's back.)   (He is in Geneva now.)

- You use the present perfect to talk about recent past events. You often use the adverbs *just, already* and *yet* with the present perfect.
  The shuttle has just landed.   *Have you already finished your work?*

- You use the present perfect to talk about an action that began in the past but is still going on now. You often use the adverbs *for* and *since* with the present perfect.
  He's had that toy for eleven years. (He's still got it.)
  We've lived in this house since 1994. (We still live here.)

Past perfect

- You use the past perfect when one past action happened before another past action.
  By the time we arrived, the bus had gone. (First the bus left, then we arrived.)

Note: You usually use the simple form (not the continuous form) with certain verbs, e.g. *agree, believe, hate, know, like, love, prefer, think, understand, want*, etc.
I was sitting by the river. I didn't know that it was full of crocodiles.
NOT   ~~I was sitting by the river. I wasn't knowing that it was full of crocodiles.~~

The future (1)

Test it ✔

1 **Find the incorrect sentences.**

   a Oh, dear. Look at the sky. It's black. It's raining later.

   b Do you think the train will be on time?

   c I think Real Madrid win the match tomorrow.

   d Don't give the kids too much pocket money. They'll only spend it on sweets.

   e Look at that man! He'll fall off that ladder.

   f Oh, no! The car's out of control. We'll crash!

   g Who do you think will win the election?

   h Next week I won't be at work. I'll be on holiday.

   i Don't leave any chocolate on the table. The dog's going to eat it.

   j I saw the boss talking to Peter this morning. I'm sure he's going to give him a pay rise.

2 **Complete the sentences. Use *going to* or *will/won't*.**

   a Don't ask Simon to fix the shelves. He .... break them. He always does.

   b Hey! Watch out! That glass .... fall off the table.

   c There's no point in giving Lucy any salad. She .... eat it.

   d I bet he .... forget my birthday again this year.

   e Tom .... go. You know he hates weddings.

   f It feels really cold. I'm sure it .... snow.

   g The twins .... be seven years old next week.

   h Oh, no! Look! Sally .... fall off her bike.

   i The bus has broken down so it .... be late.

   j Perhaps we .... meet again. Who knows?

20

GO to page 40 and check your answers.

Test it again ✅

❶ Choose the best option.

a Amy isn't going to/won't like this book. She only reads romantic novels.

b You're lucky! This time next week, you're going to/'ll be in Greece.

c Did you hear the thunder? That means there'll/'s going to be a storm.

d In a thousand years' time, dinosaurs are going to/will return to earth and eat us all up. That's what I think.

e Don't be silly. Mike and Ruth aren't going to/won't help us. They never do.

f In 2050 people aren't going to/won't live in houses.

g I'm sorry but your goldfish is very ill and it'll/'s going to die.

h When are you going to/will you know if you've passed your driving test?

i And now the weather. Tomorrow is going to/will be rainy with strong winds from the north-west.

j The cat's on the roof again. Oh, dear. Look! It'll/'s going to jump.

❷ Write sentences. Use *going to* or *will/won't*.

a Don't worry about me. I / be / OK

....

b Oh, no! There's a hole in the boat. It / sink

....

c Max! Don't give the baby a chilli! He / be / sick

....

d Great news! I / not / be / abroad / next month

....

e It / rain. Just look at that black sky

....

15

🔧 Fix it

Answers to Test it

Check your answers. Wrong answer?
Read the right Fix it note to find out why.

1 a ~~raining~~
   going to rain   → A
  b correct   → C
  c ~~win~~   will win   → B
  d correct   → B
  e ~~'ll fall~~
   's going to fall   → A
  f ~~'ll crash~~
   're going to crash   → A
  g correct   → C
  h correct   → C
  i ~~'s going to eat~~
   will eat   → B
  j correct   → A

2 a 'll   → B
  b is going to   → A
  c won't   → B
  d 'll   → B
  e won't   → B
  f 's going to   → A
  g will   → C
  h 's going to   → A
  i 's going to   → A
  j 'll   → B

Now go to page 39. Test yourself again.

Answers to Test it again

1 a won't   **f** won't
  b 'll   **g** 's going to
  c 's going to   **h** will you
  d will   **i** will
  e won't   **j** 's going to

2 a I'll be OK.
  b It's going to sink.
  c He'll be sick.
  d I won't be abroad next month.
  e It's going to rain.

🔧 Fix it notes

A
Use *going to* to make a prediction about the future because you know or can see something now.

B
Use *will* (*'ll*) and *won't* to say what you think or guess will happen in the future.

C
Use *will* (*'ll*) and *won't* to give facts about the future, or to ask questions about the future.

For more information, see the Review page opposite. ▷

 Review

The future (1)
Going to or *will*? Making predictions and talking about future facts

Unlike many other languages, English doesn't have a future tense. Instead it uses *going to, will/won't* and the present tenses. Sometimes it's difficult to know which structure to use, and often there is more than one acceptable form. This book gives guidelines to help you avoid mistakes where only one structure is possible. There are three tests on the future. They're divided like this:

The future (1) is about using *going to* and *will/won't* when you're making predictions about the future and giving or asking for information about facts in the future.

The future (2) is about using *going to* and *will/won't* when you're making decisions about the future.

The future (3) is about using *going to* and the present continuous when you're making plans for the future.

- You use *going to* to make a prediction about the future. You make the prediction because of something you know or something you can see now.
  That woman is pregnant. She's going to have a baby.
  (I can see she is pregnant now.)
  Look at that wonderful blue sky! It's going to be a nice day.
  (I can see the blue sky now so I can make a prediction about the future.)

- You use *will* (*'ll*) and *won't* to say what you think or guess will happen in the future. You don't know exactly what will happen.
  Real Madrid will win the match tomorrow.
  (That's what I think. I'm not certain.)
  The dog will eat the chocolate.
  (That's what I guess. He's done it before.)

- You use *will* (*'ll*) and *won't* to talk about things that you know about the future, or to ask questions about the future.
  I'll be twenty-seven next year.
  (This is a fact about the future. I know I'll be twenty-seven. I'm twenty-six now.)
  Will you get your exam results soon?
  (A question about a future event.)

Note: With the verb *think*, you usually say 'I don't think he will ... ' not 'I think he won't ... '
I don't think the dog will eat your supper.
NOT *I think the dog won't eat your supper.*

The future (2)

Test it ✔

① Choose the correct option, **A** or **B**.

a I .... go swimming later on. I'm leaving at two.
   A 'm going to   **B** 'll

b I can't talk now. I .... ring you this evening.
   A 'll   **B** 'm going to

c Nick and I .... see Granny when we've finished our homework.
   A will   **B** are going to

d Don't worry about the shopping. I .... it.
   A 'll do   **B** do

e I .... give up smoking. It's my New Year's resolution.
   A 'll   **B** 'm going to

f The phone's ringing. I .... answer it.
   A 'm going to   **B** 'll

g I .... have a bath. I've got some new bath oil.
   A 'm going to   **B** 'll

h We .... house as soon as we find a new one.
   A 're going to move   **B** move

i How can I get there on time? I know! I .... borrow Jim's car.
   A 'm going to   **B** 'll

j Mark says he .... study medicine at university.
   A 'll   **B** 's going to

② Complete the dialogues. Use the correct form of *going to* or *will*.

a Jean: I .... do some shopping later. Do you want anything?

   Guy: Yes, I .... have a bottle of mineral water, please.

b Lia: OK, so I .... see you in the café later then.

   Tom: No. I .... play tennis after class. See you tomorrow.

c Sid: I've had a headache all day. I .... lie down now.

   Nicky: OK. I .... bring you some aspirin in a minute.

d Carol: We .... have a party next Saturday.

   Helen: Brilliant. I .... come and help you with the food.

e Luke: I .... pick up Sue's DVD player on the way home, OK?

   Liz: Yes, that's fine. I .... ring her this afternoon
       anyway, so I can tell her then.

20

GO to page 44 and check your answers.

Test it again

1 Find the incorrect sentences.

a The dog's ill. I'll take him to the vet.

b I'll study French and Italian at university.

c We're going to have a coffee.
   I'm going to come with you.

d Do you want to go out tonight?
   No, sorry. I'll study tonight.

e Billy's cut his knee.
   You stay here. I'll get the plasters.

f We'll go to Barcelona this summer. We booked the holiday yesterday.

g Don't throw that away. I'll eat it later.

h Sarah's going to pick me up at six o'clock.

i Phil and Liz will come to dinner tomorrow. I asked them yesterday.

j Oh, dear. I've left my money at home.
   It's OK. I'll pay.

2 Which description is correct, **A** or **B**?

a Tonight I'm going to go to bed early and read.
   A decision already made   **B** sudden decision

b Jack's going to ask Sally to marry him.
   A decision already made   **B** sudden decision

c You look tired. I'll do the washing-up. You relax.
   A decision already made   **B** sudden decision

d 'The baby's crying.' 'I'll go.'
   A decision already made   **B** sudden decision

e We're going to have a barbecue on the beach. Do you want to come?
   A decision already made   **B** sudden decision

15

🔧 Fix it

Answers to Test it

Check your answers. Wrong answer?
Read the right Fix it note to find out why.

1
a A → A f B → B
b A → B g A → A
c B → A h A → A
d A → B i B → B
e B → A j B → A

2
a 'm going to → A
   'll → B
b 'll → B
   'm going to → A
c 'm going to → A
   'll → B
d 're going to → A
   'll → B
e 'll → B
   'm going to → A

◀ Now go to page 43. Test yourself again.

Answers to Test it again

1
a correct
b I'll   I'm going to
c I'm going to   I'll
d I'll   I'm going to
e correct
f We'll   We're going to
g correct
h correct
i will   are going to
j correct

2 a A b A c B d B e A

🔧 Fix it notes

A
Use *going to* to talk about decisions
you've already made for the future.

B
Use *will* to make a decision at the
moment you speak.

For more information, see the
Review page opposite. ▷

 Review

The future (2)
Going to or *will*? Making decisions about the future

In English there are two ways of talking about future decisions. You can use *going to* or you can use *will*. There is a difference:

- You use *going to* to talk about decisions you've already made for the future. Some grammar books call this 'intentions'. You intend to do something because you've made a decision to do it.
  I'm going to spend my holiday in Italy.
  (I've decided that I want to go to Italy on holiday.)
  We're going to get married next year.
  (We've decided to get married.)

  Note: When the verb *go* comes after *going to*, you often leave it out.
  I'm going to go to the shops. → *I'm going to the shops.*

- You use *will* to make a decision at the moment you speak. Some grammar books call this 'sudden' or 'spontaneous' decisions. Often you make these decisions because you're offering to do things for other people.
  'I've got no money.' 'Don't worry. I'll pay.'
  (I decide at that moment to pay.)
  'I've got a headache.' 'I'll get you some aspirin.'
  (I decide at that moment to get some aspirin.)

The future (3)

Test it ✅

1 Find the incorrect sentences.

    a When are you flying to New York?
    b Andy sees Jane at six tonight.
    c We're all meeting at Rick's place on Friday.
    d I send him an email when I get home.
    e Do you work this weekend?
    f We're travelling across the Sahara by jeep next summer.
    g I'm seeing John this afternoon, then I'm playing tennis with Ann.
    h Do you cook tonight or am I? Whose turn is it?
    i I hope you're going to quit smoking soon.
    j Can I have your credit card number? I book the tickets later.

2 Write the correct form of the verbs in brackets. Use the present continuous or *going to*.

    a I .... (see) the doctor at half-past ten tomorrow. I've got an appointment.

    b I think I .... (take) the dog to the vet soon. There's something wrong with his leg.

    c I .... (make) a sandwich in a minute. Do you want one?

    d Tonight on *Chef's World*, we .... (make) perfect pizzas. Tune in at 8.00 on BBC2 to see how it's done.

    e I .... (buy) a new mobile phone. This one's useless.

    f Jill's really excited. She .... (move) into her new home next week.

    g Tom and I .... (book) a holiday. We both need a rest.

    h Ben and Andrea .... (get) married in Paris on Saturday.

    i We've decided we .... (stop) using the car. We need to take more exercise.

    j .... (you / play) in the match this afternoon?

`20`

GO to page 48 and check your answers.

Test it again ✓

1 Is each sentence a fixed arrangement or a general plan?

	Arrangement	Plan

a I'm seeing Jim tonight. ☐ ☐
b I'm going to take up jogging. ☐ ☐

c Pippa's going to get a new job. She doesn't like the one she's got. ☐ ☐
d Pippa's getting a new job. She starts in June. ☐ ☐

e Mireia's coming round tonight for a meal. ☐ ☐
f Mireia's going to spend the summer on the Costa Brava. ☐ ☐

g We're going to start a new judo club. ☐ ☐
h We're starting a new judo class on Thursday. ☐ ☐

i I'm buying a new car. It's a silver Citroën. ☐ ☐
j Pete's going to buy his wife a diamond ring for their anniversary. ☐ ☐

2 Write sentences. Use *going to* or the present continuous.

a Jess can't come. She / play / squash / with Joe

....

b I can't meet you tomorrow. I / work / all day

....

c We / take / the kids / to Birdland / this afternoon. Do you want to come along?

....

d There's a meeting in Rome on Monday morning. He / flying / out / on Sunday

....

e You / stop / working / soon?

....

☐ 15

Fix it

Answers to Test it

Check your answers. Wrong answer?
Read the right Fix it note to find out why.

1 a correct → B
   b ~~sees~~   is seeing → B
   c correct → B
   d ~~send~~   'm going to send → A
   e ~~Do you work~~
      Are you working → B
   f correct → B
   g correct → B
   h ~~Do you cook~~
      Are you cooking → B
   i correct → A
   j ~~book~~   'm going to book → A

2 a 'm seeing → B
   b 'm going to take → A
   c 'm going to make → A
   d 're making → B
   e 'm going to buy → A
   f 's moving → B
   g are going to book → A
   h are getting → B
   i 're going to stop → A
   j Are you playing → B

Now go to page 47. Test yourself again.

Answers to Test it again

1 a arrangement   f plan
   b plan   g plan
   c plan   h arrangement
   d arrangement   i arrangement
   e arrangement   j plan

2 a She's playing squash with Joe.
   b I'm working all day.
   c We're taking the kids to Birdland
      this afternoon.
   d He's flying out on Sunday.
   e Are you going to stop working
      soon?

Fix it notes

A

Use *going to* to talk about general plans or intentions you've got for the future.

B

Use the present continuous to talk about fixed plans and arrangements you've made for the future.

> For more information, see the Review page opposite.

ⓘ Review

The future (3)
Going to or present continuous? Making plans and arrangements

In English there are two ways of talking about plans you've made. You can use *going to* or you can use the present continuous. The choice you make depends mostly on how certain the plan is. Here are some guidelines to help you choose.

* You use *going to* to talk about general plans you've made for the future. Some books call these plans 'intentions'. Often you don't say exactly when your plans will happen.
  He's going to take up swimming.
  (He's decided to take up swimming sometime soon.)
  We're going to visit our friends.
  (That's our plan. Maybe we haven't decided when we're going.)

* You use the present continuous to talk about fixed plans and arrangements you've made for the future. Often you say where or when the plan will take place.
  I'm meeting David outside the cinema at six.
  (That's what we arranged.)
  He's seeing the doctor first, then the specialist.
  (That's what he's arranged with the doctor and the specialist.)

* Sometimes it doesn't matter whether you use the present continuous or *going to*. The meaning is the same. If you're in doubt, use *going to*.
  I'm going to travel by train to Paris tomorrow.
  I'm travelling by train to Paris tomorrow.

* With the verbs *come* and *go*, it's often better to use the present continuous.
  I'm coming to see you later.   NOT   ~~I'm going to come ...~~
  He's going to Sydney.   NOT   ~~He's going to go ...~~

Test it ✔

❶ True or false?

a If I can't find a baby-sitter, I won't come tonight.
   I won't come tonight unless I find a baby-sitter.

   These two sentences mean the same thing.　　　True ☐　　　False ☐

b I'll be happy if I get the job.
   If I get the job, I'll be happy.

   One of these sentences is incorrect.　　　True ☐　　　False ☐

c If you don't marry me next year I'll scream.

   There's a very small mistake in this sentence.　　　True ☐　　　False ☐

d If I will go to Barcelona, I'll see my friends.
   If I go to Barcelona, I'll see my friends.

   Both of these sentences are correct.　　　True ☐　　　False ☐

e If I remember the number, I'll tell you.

   This sentence is about the present, not the future.　　　True ☐　　　False ☐

**❷ Complete the adverts. Use the correct form of the verbs in brackets and
will/won't where necessary.**

If you ᵃ .... *(taste)*
new **Café Délice,**
you ᵇ .... *(not want) to drink*
anything else.

You ᶜ .... (feel)
fitter than ever before if you
ᵈ .... (take) three
Supervits a day.

Your clothes ᵉ .... **(be)**
softer and fresher if you
ᶠ .... **(wash) them in**

❀ COZY ❀

If your car
ᵍ .... (break) down,

ABC Motors

ʰ .... (fix) it
free of charge!

You ⁱ .... (get) two
free bottles of champagne if you
ʲ .... (register) with
shop.com by June.

☐ 15

GO to page 52 and check your answers.

Test it again ✓

1 Write first conditional sentences.

a   I wake up early tomorrow. I go to the gym.

   ....

b   You can't go to the concert tonight. You buy a ticket.

   ....

c   She gets the job. She moves to Paris.

   ....

d   We win tomorrow's match. We have a party.

   ....

e   I go to Greece. I learn Greek.

   ....

2 Five of these sentences are incorrect. Find and correct them.

a   Unless I'll find my wallet, I won't go shopping.
b   If the Jones family moves in next door I'll move out.
c   We'll miss the plane if you don't hurry!
d   I'll send you a postcard if I'll have time.
e   Bill will break that toy if you give it to him.
f   Pam will stay in bed unless her headache gets better.
g   If Oscar goes to Italy in the summer, he learns Italian.
h   You'll have a lot more energy if you'll drink more water.
i   The children will be tired if they don't go to bed soon.
j   If anything goes wrong, I'll help you fix it.

15

🔧 Fix it

Answers to Test it

Check your answers. Wrong answer? Read the right Fix it note to find out why.

1
a True	→	E
b False	→	D
c True	→	C
d False	→	B
e False	→	A

2
a taste	→	B
b won't want	→	B
c 'll feel	→	B
d take	→	B
e will be	→	B
f wash	→	B
g breaks	→	B
h will fix	→	B
i 'll get	→	B
j register	→	B

Now go to page 51. Test yourself again.

Answers to Test it again

1
- **a** If I wake up early tomorrow, I'll go to the gym.
- **b** You can't go to the concert tonight unless you buy a ticket.
- **c** If she gets the job, she'll move to Paris.
- **d** If we win tomorrow's match, we'll have a party.
- **e** If I go to Greece, I'll learn Greek.

2
a I'll find	I find	
b door I'll	door, I'll	
c correct		
d I'll have	I have	
e correct		
f correct		
g he learns	he'll learn	
h you'll drink	you drink	
i correct		
j correct		

🔧 Fix it notes

A
Use first conditional sentences to talk about future possibilities.

B
Use the present tense in the *if*-clause and *will/won't* in the other clause in first conditional sentences.

C
When the *if*-clause comes first, put a comma between the two clauses.

D
You can reverse the two clauses of a first conditional sentence without changing the meaning.

E
Unless means the same as *if not* or *except if*.

> For more information, see the Review page opposite. ▷

 Review

First conditional

You can divide conditional sentences, sometimes called *if* sentences, into several different categories. Many people call these zero, first, second, third and mixed conditionals. They all have different uses (see page 61 and *Test it, Fix it: English Verbs and Tenses Intermediate* page 37).

- The first conditional is common when you talk about real future possibilities; things that are likely to happen.
  If I go to Barcelona, ...
  (It's possible that I'll go. I'm planning to go to Spain on holiday.)
  If I move to London, ...
  (It's possible that I'll move. I'm looking for a job in London.)

- You use the present tense in the *if* clause and *will/won't* in the other clause in first conditional sentences to talk about the future. Don't use *will/won't* in both clauses. This is a very common mistake.
  If it's sunny, we'll have a barbecue.
  NOT ~~If it'll be sunny, we'll have a barbecue.~~
  If you send me a card, I'll be very happy.
  NOT ~~If you'll send me a card, I'll be very happy.~~

- The *if* clause often comes first. However, you can reverse the two clauses of a first conditional sentence without changing the meaning.
  If Pat doesn't arrive soon, we'll go.
  = *We'll go if Pat doesn't arrive soon.*
  She'll get a pay rise if she works hard.
  = *If she works hard, she'll get a pay rise.*

- When the *if* clause comes first, you put a comma between the two clauses. You don't need one if it comes second.
  If it rains, I'll stay at home.
  I'll stay at home if it rains.

  Note, however, that native speakers often leave the comma out. You may see examples of this in newspapers and magazines, and on the internet.

- *Unless* means the same as *if not* or *except if*.
  I won't pass my exam unless I work harder.
  = *If I don't work harder, I won't pass my exam.*

All future forms

Test it ✔

❶ Write the correct future forms in the gaps. If two forms are possible, write both.

Roger: I ᵃ...................................... (run) in the London marathon.

Daniel: Wow! I didn't know that. I ᵇ...................................... (come) and watch you.

Roger: OK. I ᶜ...................................... (leave) the house at about six so I'll pick
          you up on the way.

Daniel: Your children ᵈ...................................... (be) excited, won't they? They
          might even see you on TV!

Roger: Yes. But they're sure I ᵉ...................................... (finish) last! I often do.

Daniel: If you finish last, they ᶠ...................................... (not / speak) to you ever
          again. How embarrassing!

Roger: Don't worry, I won't. I ᵍ...................................... (train) in the gym all day
          tomorrow and on Saturday.

Daniel: I saw James's name on the list, so he ʰ...................................... (run) too.
          I bet you ⁱ...................................... (not / run) faster than him. If you do, I
          ʲ...................................... (be) amazed. He's *really* fit!

❷ Find and correct five mistakes.

a   Look at that blue sky!
        It'll be a nice day.
              Brilliant! Let's go surfing!

b   Next week my wife is going
        to be on holiday in Italy.
              How nice. And you'll
              be here at the office!

c   I think Real Madrid are
        winning the match on Saturday.
              No way! Barcelona will win.
              I'm sure.

d   If it rains this afternoon,
        we take the kids swimming.
              Good idea.

e   I can't understand
        this software at all.
              Can't you? Don't worry.
              I'm helping you.

[15]

GO to page 56 and check your answers.

Test it again ✓

❶ Choose the best option, A or B.

a In June I .... thirty-seven.   **A** 'll be   **B** 'm being
b Don't carry those heavy bags. I .... it.   **A** 'm doing   **B** 'll do
c We .... Karl and Myles this evening.   **A** 'll meet   **B** 're meeting
d Watch out! You .... off that ladder!   **A** 're going to fall   **B** 're falling
e I've decided I .... some fish today.   **A** cook   **B** 'm going to cook

❷ Write sentences. Use the correct future form. If two answers are possible, write both.

a I / think / be / sunny / tomorrow

  ....

b That man / crash / his car!

  ....

c This time next week / you / be / on holiday

  ....

d I / do / the shopping / for you

  ....

e Liz / meet / Johnny / tonight

  ....

f If / you / wash / the plates / I / dry / them

  ....

g I'm certain / my brother / be / famous / one day

  ....

h We've decided / we / buy / a new car

  ....

i Harry / break / anything / you / give / him

  ....

j I hope / we / meet / again

  ....

15

Fix it

Answers to Test it

Check your answers. Wrong answer?
Read the right Fix it note to find out why.

1
  a 'm going to run   → A
  b 'll come   → D
  c 'm leaving   → C
  d will be   → E
  e 'll finish   → E
  f won't speak   → G
  g 'm training   → C
  h 's going to run   → B
  i won't run   → E
  j 'll be   → G

2
  a ~~'ll be~~
    's going to be   → B
  b ~~is going to be~~   will be   → F
  c ~~are winning~~   will win   → E
  d ~~we take~~   we'll take → G
  e ~~I'm helping~~   I'll help   → D

Now go to page 55. Test yourself again.

Answers to Test it again

1
  a A   **b** B   **c** B   **d** A   **e** B

2
  a I think it'll be sunny tomorrow.
  b That man's going to crash his car!
  c This time next week you'll be on
     holiday.
  d I'll do the shopping for you.
  e Liz is meeting/is going to meet
     Johnny tonight.
  f If you wash the plates, I'll dry
     them.
  g I'm certain my brother will be
     famous one day.
  h We've decided we're going to
     buy a new car.
  i Harry will break anything you
     give him.
  j I hope we'll meet again.

Fix it notes

A
Use *going to* to talk about general
plans you've already made for the
future.

B
Use *going to* to make a prediction
about the future based on something
you know or can see now.

C
Use the present continuous to talk
about fixed plans and arrangements
you've made for the future, especially
when you mention a time or place.

D
Use *will* to make a decision at the
moment you speak.

E
Use *will* (*'ll*) and *won't* to say what you
think or guess will happen in the future.

F
Use *will* (*'ll*) and *won't* to talk about
future facts, or to ask questions about
the future.

G
Use *will* to talk about future
possibilities in first conditional
sentences. Use the present tense in the
if-clause and *will* or *won't* in the other
clause.

For more information, see the
Review page opposite.

 Review

All future forms

Going to

- You use *going to* to talk about general plans you've already made for the future.
  I'm going to take up swimming.   *We're going to visit our friends.*

- You also use *going to* to make logical predictions about the future based on things you know or can see now.
  That woman is pregnant. She's going to have a baby.

Present continuous

- You use the present continuous to talk about fixed plans and arrangements you've made for the future. Often you mention the time or place.
  I'm meeting David outside the cinema at six.
  (That's what we arranged.)
  He's spending a month in Egypt and then going to Morocco.
  (That's what he's arranged.)

Note: Sometimes it doesn't matter whether you use the present continuous or *going to*. The meaning is the same. If you're in doubt, use *going to*.
I'm going to travel by train to Paris tomorrow.
I'm travelling by train to Paris tomorrow.

Will

- You use *will* to make a decision at the moment you speak. Often you're offering to do something for someone.
  I'll pay for that.   *I'll come with you.*   *I'll get you some aspirin.*

- You use *will* (*'ll*) and *won't* to say what you think or guess will happen.
  Real Madrid will win the match tomorrow. (That's what I think.)
  The dog will eat the chocolate. (That's what I guess. He's done it before.)

- You can use *will* (*'ll*) and *won't* to talk about future facts, or to ask questions about the future.
  You won't be on holiday next week. You'll be at work.
  He'll be forty next month.
  Will you get your exam results soon?

- You use *will* and *won't* to talk about future possibilities in first conditional sentences.
  If I go to Barcelona, I'll see my friend's new baby. (It's possible that I'll go.)

Present tenses with time expressions, etc.

Test it ✔

① Find the correct sentence in each group.

a I'll get some milk when I'll go to the shops.
b I'll get some milk when I go to the shops.
c I get some milk when I will go to the shops.

d We're going to wait until he'll phone.
e We're going to wait until he's phoning.
f We're going to wait until he phones.

g You turn left at the traffic lights, then you'll go straight on.
h You will turn left at the traffic lights, then you'll go straight on.
i You turn left at the traffic lights, then you go straight on.

j If you'll heat ice, it'll melt.
k If you heat ice, it melts.
l If you'll heat ice, it melts.

m Sasha's going to meet us after she's seen Mike.
n Sasha's going to meet us after she'll see Mike.
o Sasha's going to meet us after she's going to see Mike.

② Choose the best option.

a When I will grow up/grow up, I'm going to be a train driver.
b She'll tell me when the painting is/will be finished.
c Where will/do I pay for this?
d When does/will the 09.25 train arrive in Cambridge?
e If you will mix/mix blue and yellow, you get green.
f After he passes/will pass his exams, he'll be a doctor.
g Let's play until it will get/gets dark.
h I'll plant these flowers as soon as it will stop/stops raining.
i Please don't forget to phone before you leave/will leave.
j You put the key in the lock and you will turn/turn it to the left.

15

GO to page 60 and check your answers.

Test it again ✅

1 Choose the best option, **A** or **B**.

a Don't worry. I .... the children to school.
A take   **B** 'll take

b After you .... smoking, you'll notice that you feel much better.
A will stop   **B** stop

c Where .... the tickets?
A do I buy   **B** will I buy

d In the future people .... their holidays on space stations.
A spend   **B** will spend

e If it stops raining soon, we .... out.
A 'll go   **B** go

f Wait a minute! I .... with you.
A come   **B** 'll come

g You break the eggs and you .... them to the mixture.
A add   **B** 'll add

h We won't get married until we .... better jobs.
A 'll have   **B** have

i When you .... better we'll have a party to celebrate.
A 'll feel   **B** feel

j If you .... sad, I'm sad.
A 're   **B** 'll be

2 Five of these sentences are incorrect. Find and correct them.

a You're on the wrong bus. This one won't stop at Birmingham.

f If you'll go out in the snow, you get cold.

b The cat will stay out until it'll get cold.

g The plane takes off at one.

c I'll tell him when I'll see him.

h Let's go before it'll rain.

d How do you play this game?

i As soon as the exams are over, I'm leaving school.

e OK, so what do I do now?

j We'll call when we get home.

15

🔧 Fix it

Answers to Test it

Check your answers. Wrong answer?
Read the right Fix it note to find out why.

1 The correct sentences are:

b → A		k → F	
f → E		m→ C	
i → H			

2
a grow up	→ A
b is	→ A
c do	→ H
d does	→ A, G
e mix	→ F
f passes	→ C
g gets	→ E
h stops	→ B
i leave	→ D
j turn	→ H

Now go to page 59. Test yourself again.

Answers to Test it again

1
a B	b B	c A	d B	e A
f B	g A	h B	i B	j A

2
a won't stop	doesn't stop
b it'll get	it gets
c 'll see	see
d correct	
e correct	
f you'll go	you go
g correct	
h 'll rain	rains
i correct	
j correct	

🔧 Fix it notes

A
Use the present simple after *when* to talk about the future.

B
Use the present simple after *as soon as* when you mean 'immediately after'.

C
Use the present simple or the present perfect simple in clauses with *after* to talk about the future.

D
Use the present simple in clauses with *before* to talk about the future.

E
Use the present simple after *until* to talk about a time between now and the future.

F
Use the present simple after *if* when the statement is always true.

G
Use the present simple to talk about scheduled future events, especially timetables.

H
Use the present simple to give people instructions, and to ask for instructions.

For more information, see the Review page opposite. ▷

 Review

Present tenses with time expressions, etc.

You use the present simple mostly to talk about routines and habits (see page 9) but you also use it in other circumstances. You often use the present simple to talk about the future, in 'zero conditional' sentences, and when you give people instructions. Here are the most common uses of it.

- You use the present simple (not *will*) after *when* to talk about the future.
  Buy some milk when you go out.   NOT   ~~... when you'll go out.~~
  I'll tell him when I see him.   NOT   ~~... when I'll see him.~~

- You use the present simple after *as soon as* when you mean 'immediately after'. Again, you're talking about a future event. You don't use *will* or *going to*.
  I'll cook some food as soon as the programme ends.
  NOT   ~~... as soon as the programme will/is going to end.~~

- You use the present simple or the present perfect simple in clauses with *after* to talk about the future. There is no difference in meaning between the two tenses. You can use either.
  After he passes his exams, he'll be a doctor.   NOT   ~~... after he will pass~~
  After the movie has ended, we'll go home.   NOT   ~~... after the movie will end~~

- You use the present simple in clauses with *before* to talk about the future.
  Remember to call me before you come.   NOT   ~~... before you will come.~~

- You use the present simple after *until* to talk about a time between now and the future.
  Let's play until it gets dark.   NOT   ~~... until it'll get dark.~~
  I won't help you until you say 'please'.

- You use the present simple after *if* when the statement is always true. Some books call these sentences 'zero conditional' sentences. You use the present simple in both clauses.
  If you heat ice, it melts.   *If you smile, I feel happy.*

- You often use the present simple to talk about scheduled future events, especially timetables.
  When does the bus leave Paris?   *The exam starts at nine.*

- You use the present simple to give people instructions or directions, and to ask for instructions.
  You turn left, then you go straight on.
  I've turned the machine on. Now what do I do?
  Where can I go for help?

Obligation and necessity

Test it ✔

1 Choose the best option.

a He musted/had to start work at six every morning when he was a postman.

b You have to/mustn't work hard to be successful.

c You needn't/mustn't eat those leaves. They might be poisonous.

d I'm happy because I mustn't/needn't get up early tomorrow.

e You don't have to/mustn't smoke in the library.

f She hadn't to/didn't have to wear a uniform.

g I must/have to remember to pay the phone bill.

h Hey! You mustn't to/mustn't park there. It's private!

i You needn't/have to drive on the left in the UK.

j I must/must to take more exercise.

2 Find the incorrect sentences.

a We mustn't be late for the lecture.

b You must lose some weight.

c Caroline doesn't have to work on Saturdays.

d You mustn't go now but you can if you want to.

e Mark hasn't to worry about the exam—he's done lots of work.

f You don't have to stay out later than ten. That's when they lock the door.

g You needn't drink water from the river: it's dirty.

h Relax! We mustn't leave till ten o'clock.

i You have to leave your bags at the desk.

j You'll must find a job very soon.

I must lose some weight . . .

20

GO to page 64 and check your answers.

Test it again ✔

① Match the statements.

a	You mustn't buy me a present.	1	You can go if you want to.
b	You don't have to leave.	2	Don't forget to buy me a present.
c	You have to stay.	3	You mustn't leave.
d	You mustn't eat that.	4	You needn't eat your vegetables.
e	You can't leave your vegetables!	5	You needn't buy me a present.
f	You mustn't smoke.	6	You can stay if you like.
g	You don't have to buy me a present.	7	You can't eat that.
h	You must remember to buy me a present.	8	You definitely shouldn't buy me a present.
i	You don't have to eat your vegetables.	9	You must eat your vegetables.
j	You don't have to stay.	10	You can't smoke.

② Find the correct sentence in each pair.

a I didn't have to sell the house.
b I needn't to sold the house.

c You don't have to get angry. It's bad for your heart.
d You mustn't get angry. It's bad for your heart.

e He'll have to tell the police.
f He will must tell the police.

g You needn't talk to strangers. It could be dangerous.
h You mustn't talk to strangers. It could be dangerous.

i Janet mustn't ring me–I've found the number I wanted.
j Janet needn't ring me–I've found the number I wanted.

15

🔧 Fix it

Answers to Test it

Check your answers. Wrong answer?
Read the right Fix it note to find out why.

1
  a had to   → D
  b have to   → E
  c mustn't   → B
  d needn't   → F
  e mustn't   → B
  f didn't have to   → F
  g must   → C
  h mustn't   → G, B
  i have to   → E
  j must   → G, C

2
  a correct   → C
  b correct   → A
  c correct   → F
  d ~~mustn't~~
  don't have to/needn't → F
  e ~~hasn't to~~
  needn't/doesn't have to → F
  f ~~don't have to~~
  mustn't   → B
  g ~~needn't~~   mustn't   → B
  h ~~mustn't~~
  needn't/don't have to → F
  i correct   → E
  j ~~'ll must~~   'll have to   → D

> Now go to page 63. Test yourself again.

Answers to Test it again

1   **a** 8   **b** 6   **c** 3   **d** 7   **e** 9
    f 10   **g** 5   **h** 2   **i** 4   **j** 1

2 The correct sentences are:
    a   **d**   **e**   **h**   **j**

🔧 Fix it notes

A
Use *must* to give people orders or to make strong suggestions.

B
Use *mustn't* to give people negative orders or to tell them about a negative order.

C
Use *must* and *mustn't* to talk about an obligation you feel.

D
Must has no past or future form. Use *had to* and *will have to*.

E
Use *have to* to talk about obligations that come from other people.

F
Use *don't have to* or *needn't* to say that something is unnecessary.

G
Use the base form of the verb after *must* and *needn't*.

> For more information, see the
> Review page opposite. ▷

i Review

Obligation and necessity

Must and *mustn't*

- You use *must* to give people orders or to make strong suggestions. This is especially common when you are in a position of authority, e.g. a parent talking to a child.
  You must be home by ten! (You can't stay out later than ten.)
  You must listen to me. (You can't not listen to me.)

- You use *mustn't* to give a negative order to someone or to tell them about a negative order.
  You mustn't talk to strangers. (You can't talk to strangers. It might be dangerous.)
  You mustn't park here. (You can't park here. There's a 'No parking' sign.)

- You also use *must* and *mustn't* to talk about an obligation you feel.
  I must post this letter.   *We mustn't be late for the lecture.*

Have to, don't have to and *needn't*

- You use *have to* to talk about obligations that come from other people. Often the 'other people' are the police, the government, the law, teachers, etc. In the positive form, *have to* is very similar in meaning to *must*.
  You have to drive on the left.
  (You can't drive on the right. The law says you must drive on the left.)

- You use *don't have to* and *needn't* to say that something is unnecessary.
  I don't have to get up early tomorrow. (It isn't necessary.)
  You needn't get up early tomorrow.

Note: *Don't have to* is very different in meaning from *mustn't*.
You mustn't leave. (You can't leave. You have no choice.)
You don't have to leave. (You can stay or go. It's your choice.)

Form of *must, have to* and *needn't*

- Be careful! *Must* hasn't got a past or future form. You use *had to* to talk about the past and *will have to* to talk about the future.
  He had to start work at six.   NOT   *He musted start ...*
  You'll have to find a job.   NOT   *You'll must find a job.*

- You use the infinitive without *to* after *must* and *needn't*.
  You must call me.   NOT   *You must to call me.*
  You mustn't smoke.   NOT   *You mustn't to smoke.*
  You needn't worry.   NOT   *You needn't to worry.*

Ability

Test it ✔

1 Find and correct five mistakes.

a Peter was locked in for five hours but luckily he could escape through a window.

b My son couldn't read until he was eight but now he reads all the time.

c Next year we'll have more money. Then we manage to get married.

d When we arrived in the city centre, no one managed to tell us where the hotel was.

e When John passes his test, he'll manage to drive the kids to school.

f Can you understand these instructions?

g The thieves managed to break into the car even though it was alarmed.

h I'll be able to come and stay with you more often when I retire.

i Last year I can't speak Spanish but now I can.

j Why can't you tell me the truth for once?

2 Use the correct forms of the expressions to fill the gaps. Sometimes two answers are possible.

be able to   can   can't   could   couldn't   manage to

a When I was little, I .... ride a bike but I could swim.

b The car broke down but the mechanic .... fix it after a while.

c .... you use spreadsheets on the computer?

d Next year, I .... afford a new car.

e No one .... tell me where the post office was.

f I'm sorry but I .... help you today. I'm too busy.

g .... you really speak two languages when you were six?

h The survivors of the crash .... escape from the plane seconds before it exploded.

i I'm afraid we .... get to Brussels by tomorrow– it's already very late.

j Sonia's amazing. She's only ten and she .... already play five instruments.

15

GO to page 68 and check your answers.

Test it again ✓

① Choose the correct option, **A** or **B**.

a We .... find the house by looking at the map and asking for directions.
A could **B** managed to

b In ten years' time, people .... spend holidays in space.
A will be able to **B** can

c I don't understand why Zack .... come to see me yesterday.
A can't **B** couldn't

d Most people these days .... use the internet.
A can **B** could

e None of us .... understand a word the teacher was saying.
A can **B** could

f .... rescue your cat?
A Could you **B** Did you manage to

g .... come to my wedding in June?
A Will you be able to **B** Will you manage to

h My parents .... understand why I like the band *Slipknot*.
A won't be able to **B** can't

i .... look after my dog while I'm away?
A Will you manage to **B** Will you be able to

j Jay .... drive a car and fly a plane now that he's got his licences.
A could **B** can

② Complete the sentences. Use the correct form of *can, could, be able to* or *managed to*.

a My grandmother .... walk for two months after she'd broken her leg.

b Our dog fell into the river but we .... rescue him.

c Luckily, I .... get a refund for the ticket.

d Do you think scientists .... find a cure for cancer one day?

e .... you read when you were five?

15

Fix it

Answers to Test it

Check your answers. Wrong answer?
Read the right Fix it note to find out why.

1
a ~~could~~
managed to/was able to → D
b correct → B
c ~~manage to get~~
'll be able to get → C
d ~~managed to~~ could → B
e ~~manage to~~ be able to → C
f correct → A
g correct → D
h correct → C
i ~~can't~~ couldn't → B
j correct → A

2
a couldn't → B
b managed to/was able to → D
c Can → A
d 'll be able to → C
e could → B
f can't → A
g Could → B
h managed to/were able to → D
i won't be able to → C
j can → A

Now go to page 67. Test yourself again.

Answers to Test it again

1 a B **b** A **c** B **d** A **e** B
f B **g** A **h** B **i** B **j** B

2 a couldn't
b managed to/were able to
c managed to/was able to
d will be able to
e Could

Fix it notes

A
Use *can* and *can't* to talk about ability in the present.

B
Use *could* and *couldn't* to talk about general ability in the past.

C
Use *will* or *won't be able to* to talk about ability in the future.

D
Use *managed to* or *was/were able to* (not *could*) to talk about ability on a particular occasion in the past.

For more information, see the Review page opposite.

ⓘ Review

Ability

There are several different ways of talking about ability in English. The choice of words you use depends on whether you're talking about the present, the past or the future. It can also depend on whether you're talking about general ability or ability on a particular occasion.

- You use *can* and *can't* to talk about ability in the present. *Can* and *can't* are followed by the base form of the verb only. Don't use *to* + base form of the verb.
  I can ride a bike.　　　　　　NOT　*I can to ride a bike.*
  She can't use spreadsheets.　NOT　*She can't to use spreadsheets.*

- You use *could* and *couldn't* to talk about general ability in the past.
  He could speak two languages when he was six.
  Jane couldn't type until she bought a computer.

- You use *will/won't be able* to to talk about ability in the future. There's no future form of *can*.
  I'll be able to see you more often when I've retired.
  We won't be able to afford a holiday next year.

- You use *managed to* or *was/were able to* (not *could*) to talk about ability on a particular occasion in the past, often when something was difficult to do.
  The survivors managed to/were able to escape from the plane.
  NOT　*The survivors could ...*
  He managed to/was able to fix the car.
  NOT　*He could fix the car.*

-ing form or infinitive?

Test it ✓

1 Choose the best option, **A** or **B**.

a Are you interested in .... to the party with us?
   A to come   **B** coming

b I'm looking forward to .... you again soon.
   A see   **B** seeing

c Oh, no! I forgot .... Jim's birthday card.
   A to post   **B** posting

d Sam wants .... on holiday.
   A to go   **B** going

e Are you thinking of .... your job?
   A to change   **B** changing

f Sue regrets .... school at fifteen.
   A to leave   **B** leaving

g I always enjoy .... the cuckoo in the spring.
   A to hear   **B** hearing

h My friend is giving up .... at last.
   A to smoke   **B** smoking

i We stopped .... because we were tired.
   A to rest   **B** resting

j You can't sneeze without .... your eyes.
   A to close   **B** closing

2 Find the incorrect sentences.

a Tom always insists on to cook.

b I enjoy to get up early.

c Thank you for telling me about it.

d I expect getting a pay rise soon.

e I can't stand to pay for bad food.

f They agreed being friends again.

g Helen hopes being a movie star.

h Would you like having a cup of coffee?

i We feel like going out for a walk.

j I suggest to stay here.

k They managed finding the hotel.

l I dislike to swim as much as running.

m He didn't remember meeting my mother.

n Did you forget to phone her?

24

GO to page 72 and check your answers.

70

Test it again ✓

1 Write the correct form of the verbs in brackets. Use the *-ing* form or infinitive.
If both forms are possible, write both.

a I regret .... (tell) you about my problem.

b He's learning .... (cook).

c Do you really need .... (work) tonight?

d He's fed up with .... (drive) his old car.

e She couldn't live without .... (see) him every day.

f Both children are keen on .... (play) football.

g Did you remember .... (let) the cat out last night?

h They stopped .... (put) the tent up.

i Mike really dislikes .... (dance).

j I'd love .... (travel) more.

2 Put each verb in the correct group.

agree	decide	enjoy	expect	finish
forget	give up	go	hate	hope
learn	love	like	need	regret
remember	stop	suggest	want	would love

+ *-ing* form	+ infinitive	+ *-ing* form or infinitive

☐ 30

🔧 Fix it

Answers to Test it
Check your answers. Wrong answer?
Read the right Fix it note to find out why.

①	a B → A	f B → D
	b B → A	g B → B
	c A → D	h B → A
	d A → C	i A → D
	e B → A	j B → A

②	a	to cook	cooking	→ A
	b	to get	getting up	→ B
	c	correct		→ A
	d	getting	to get	→ C
	e	to pay	paying	→ B
	f	being	to be	→ C
	g	being	to be	→ C
	h	having	to have	→ C
	i	correct		→ A
	j	to stay	staying	→ B
	k	finding	to find	→ C
	l	to swim	swimming	→ B
	m	correct		→ D
	n	correct		→ D

◀ Now go to page 71. Test yourself again.

Answers to Test it again

①	a telling	f playing
	b to cook	g to let
	c to work	h putting/to put
	d driving	i dancing
	e seeing	j to travel

② **+ -ing form**
enjoy, finish, give up, go, hate, like,
love, suggest

+ infinitive
agree, decide, expect, hope, learn,
need, want, would love

+ -ing form or infinitive
forget, regret, remember, stop

🔧 Fix it notes

A
Use the *-ing* form (not the infinitive)
after a preposition, e.g. *for, in, like, of,
on, to, up, without,* etc.

B
Use the *-ing* form (not the infinitive)
after some verbs, e.g. *can't stand,
dislike, enjoy, suggest,* etc.

C
Use the infinitive (not the *-ing* form)
after some verbs, e.g. *agree, expect,
hope, manage, want, would like,* etc.

D
Use the *-ing* form or the infinitive after
some verbs, e.g. *forget, regret,
remember, stop.* Be careful! The
meaning of the verb changes.

> For more information, see the
> Review page opposite. ▷

ⓘ Review

-ing form or infinitive?

Using the *-ing* form

- You use the *-ing* form of the verb (not the infinitive) after prepositions, e.g. *about, at, in, of, on, to, without*, etc.
  Both my children are interested in making models.
  David is thinking of writing a book.

- You use the *-ing* form (not the infinitive) after some verbs, e.g. *can't stand, dislike, enjoy, finish, give up, go, hate, like, love, suggest*, etc. The verb *go* is very common when you talk about sports.
  Let's go jogging on the beach.   *He dislikes cooking.*
  Max suggested watching a movie.   *I'll finish doing this, then I'll help you.*

Using the infinitive

- You use the infinitive (not the *-ing* form) after these verbs: *agree, decide, expect, hope, learn, manage, need, promise, want, would like/love/hate,* etc.
  I want to learn another language.   *They promised to come back soon.*
  We agreed to meet on Friday.   *I'd hate to be a zookeeper.*

Verbs that take both the *-ing* form and infinitive

- You can use the *-ing* form or the infinitive after some verbs, e.g. *forget, regret, remember, stop*. But be careful! There is a change of meaning.
  stop
  Phil stopped to say hello. (He stopped what he was doing because he wanted to say 'hello'.)
  Phil stopped saying he was bored. (He said he was bored for a long time. Then he stopped saying it.)
  forget
  I forgot to lock the door. (It's unlocked.)
  I'll never forget seeing the Nile for the first time. (It's an important memory.)
  remember
  Do you remember meeting me for the first time? (Is it a memory you have?)
  Did you remember to lock the door? (Sometimes you forget.)
  regret
  I regret shouting at him. (I shouted. I'm sorry that I did.)
  I regret to say you're fired. (I'm going to tell you you're fired. I'm sorry about it.)

Do, make, have and have got

Test it ✔

1 Complete the sentences. Use the correct form of *do* or *make*.

a Have you .... your homework yet?

b Mum .... the beds, then she tidies the kitchen.

c Oh, no! I've .... a terrible mistake.

d Sometimes I just .... nothing.

e I'd like to .... some walking on holiday.

f George is good at .... paper aeroplanes.

g Sarah .... a phone call and then went out.

h He's hurt himself! Somebody .... something!

i Shall I .... you a sandwich?

j I'll .... the shopping this week.

Some days I don't do much, I just hang out with my friends . . .

2 Choose the best option.

a Have you/Have you got any brothers or sisters?

b I've got/I have a really bad headache.

c Do you have/Have you got lunch at one every day?

d I'm single. I haven't/haven't got a husband.

e Sally has/has got brown eyes.

f I'd got/I had a lovely dream last night.

g Has the hotel/Has the hotel got a swimming pool?

h We have/We've got a maths class every Tuesday.

i Do you often have/Have you often got a day off work?

j Ouch! I have/I've got something in my eye.

20

GO to page 76 and check your answers.

Test it again ✅

① Choose the best option, **A** or **B**.

a I feel terrible. I .... a cold and a sore throat.
  A 've got **B** have

b What do you want to .... this evening?
  A make **B** do

c Wendy .... a wonderful Spanish omelette for us last night.
  A did **B** made

d .... breakfast this morning?
  A Had you got **B** Did you have

e We .... a teachers' meeting every Friday afternoon. It's so boring.
  A 've got **B** have

f Hurry up and .... your hair. We're going to be late.
  A do **B** make

g I've met a man who .... two houses.
  A has **B** 's got

h .... geography lessons at your school?
  A Have you got **B** Do you have

i First I .... the ironing, then I made the beds.
  A did **B** made

j Can I .... a suggestion? Let's go to the beach.
  A make **B** do

② Match the two halves of each sentence.

a	Sally's got	**1** any children?
b	Isn't it time you did	**2** two cats and a dog.
c	Why don't you make	**3** mistakes.
d	Jill never has	**4** your best.
e	I rarely make	**5** nothing all day.
f	You can only do	**6** that noise!
g	Please stop making	**7** a cup of tea?
h	Do you ever have	**8** lunch. She's too busy.
i	Haven't you got	**9** some work?
j	John's lazy. He does	**10** breakfast in bed?

20

🔧 Fix it

Answers to Test it

Check your answers. Wrong answer?
Read the right Fix it note to find out why.

1
a done	→	A
b makes	→	E
c made	→	E
d do	→	B
e do	→	C
f making	→	D
g made	→	E
h do	→	B
i make	→	D
j do	→	C

2
a Have you got	→	H
b I've got	→	H
c Do you have	→	G
d haven't got	→	H
e has got	→	H
f I had	→	F
g Has the hotel got	→	H
h We have	→	G
i Do you often have	→	G
j I've got	→	H

◀ Now go to page 75. Test yourself again.

Answers to Test it again

1
a A	**b** B	**c** B	**d** B	**e** B
f A	**g** B	**h** B	**i** A	**j** A

2
a 2	**b** 9	**c** 7	**d** 8	**e** 3
f 4	**g** 6	**h** 10	**i** 1	**j** 5

🔧 Fix it notes

A
Use *do* to talk about things connected with work.

B
Use *do* when you don't want to or can't describe the activity fully.

C
Use *do* before a determiner (*some, the,* etc.) + *-ing* form.

D
Use *make* to talk about things you create.

E
Use *make* in certain fixed expressions.

F
Use *have* + object to talk about experiences and actions.

G
Use *have* to talk about events that happen regularly.

H
Use *have got* to talk about possessions, relationships and to describe people. Also use it to talk about illnesses or physical problems.

> For more information, see the Review page opposite. ▷

 **Review**

Do, make, have and *have got*

The words *make* and *do*, and *have* and *have got* can cause problems for learners because it's easy to confuse them. Often they appear in fixed expressions which you just have to learn as you go along. However, there are a few general rules.

Do

- You use *do* in the following ways:
  to talk about things connected with work or household tasks.
  Have you done your homework?   I've got to do my business plan.
  I hate doing the washing-up.
  when you don't want to or can't describe the activity fully.
  Somebody do something!   Sometimes I just do nothing.
  before a determiner (*some, any, the*, etc.) + *-ing* form.
  I'll do the shopping this week.   Did you do any sightseeing?
  in certain fixed expressions.
  Do business with someone.   Do your best.   Do good.
  Do your make up/hair.   Do your duty.   Do someone a favour.

Make

- You use *make* in the following ways:
  to talk about things you create.
  Shall I make you a sandwich?   He's good at making paper aeroplanes.
  in a lot of fixed expressions.
  Make a phone call.   Make the bed.   Make a mistake.   Make a fuss.
  Make a noise.   Make an effort.   Make a suggestion.   Make money.

Have

- You use *have* + object in the following ways:
  to talk about experiences and actions.
  Do you have lunch at one?   He's having a bath.   I had a lovely dream.
  Did you have a good sleep?   He's had an accident.   Let's have a swim.
  to talk about events that happen regularly, especially but not always timetabled or scheduled events.
  We have a maths class every Tuesday.   Do you often have bad headaches?

Have got

- You use *have got* to talk about possessions, relationships and to describe people. You can also use it to talk about illnesses or physical problems.
  Have you got a car?   She's got two brothers and a sister.
  Pete's got flu.   Ouch! I've got something in my eye.

Reported speech

Test it ✔

1 Match the reported speech to the direct speech.

a	He said he was enjoying the party.	'I was enjoying the party.'
		'I enjoy parties.'
		'I'm enjoying the party.'
b	They told us they might go to Spain.	'We may go to Spain.'
		'We're going to Spain.'
		'We go to Spain.'
c	Mike said it had snowed a lot.	'It's snowing a lot.'
		'It snows a lot.'
		'It's snowed a lot.'
d	Lisse said she'd be late tonight.	'She'll be late tonight.'
		'I'll be late tonight.'
		'I'd be late tonight.'
e	Nick said he'd seen you in the bank.	'I saw you in the bank.'
		'I saw her in the bank.'
		'I see you in the bank.'

2 Find and correct the mistakes.

   a I said him I liked his car.
   b Katie told she wanted to marry Arthur.
   c Pam said I spoke Italian. She grew up in Florence.
   d They said they will wait for us at the library but they didn't.
   e Pete said Kay he couldn't go on holiday with her.

|10|

GO to page 80 and check your answers.

Test it again ✔

1 Rewrite these sentences as direct speech.

a The boy said he was playing football.

....

b My daughter told me her toes were cold.

....

c Stephen said he'd carry my suitcase.

....

d They told us they were going on holiday that day.

....

e Dad said he wanted to sit in this chair.

....

2 Choose *said* or *told*.

a The teacher .... she couldn't hear the answer.

b Patrick .... me he was getting married.

c Christine .... that she liked travelling.

d They .... us we could use their car.

e He .... he loved her.

3 Rewrite what this teenager is saying. Use reported speech. Begin 'She said'.

'Nobody understands me. My brother doesn't listen to me, my dog hates me and my parents think I'm crazy. They won't let me go out at night and I can't play loud music after midnight. Our house is too small for four people! I'm going to leave home and live with my boyfriend.'

30

Fix it

Answers to Test it

Check your answers. Wrong answer?
Read the right Fix it note to find out why.

1 **a** 'I'm enjoying the party.'   → A
  b 'We may go to Spain.'   → C
  c 'It's snowed a lot.'   → A
  d 'I'll be late tonight.'   → A, B
  e 'I saw her in the bank.'   → A, B

2 **a** I ~~said~~ told him/
    I said ~~him~~ I liked   → D, E
  b Katie ~~told~~ said she/
    Katie told me she   → D, E
  c Pam said ~~t~~ she spoke   → B
  d They said they ~~will~~
    would wait   → C
  e Pete ~~said~~ told Kay   → D, E

Now go to page 79. Test yourself again.

Answers to Test it again

1 **a** I'm playing football.
  b My toes are cold!
  c I'll carry your suitcase.
  d We're going on holiday today.
  e I want to sit in this chair.

2 **a** said   **b** told   **c** said
  d told   **e** said

3 She said nobody understood her.
She said her brother didn't listen to
her, her dog hated her and her
parents thought she was crazy. She
said they wouldn't let her go out at
night and she couldn't play loud
music after midnight. She said their
house was too small for four
people. She said she was going to
leave home and live with her
boyfriend.

Fix it notes

A
Usually go back a tense when you
report speech.

B
Change the pronouns when you report
speech.

C
Change *can* to *could* and *will* to *would*
in reported speech. Change *may* to
might.

D
Always put a personal direct object or a
name after *tell*.

E
Never put a personal direct object
after *say*.

For more information, see the
Review page opposite.

 Review

Reported speech

When you report speech, you usually need to go back a tense.

I'm cold. (present simple)	*She said she was cold.* (past simple)
I'm reading. (present continuous)	*He said he was reading.* (past continuous)
I read a book. (past simple)	*She said she'd read a book.* (past perfect)
We've been to Oslo. (present perfect)	*They said they'd been to Oslo.* (past perfect)
I'd met Lucy before. (past perfect)	*John said he'd met Lucy before.* (past perfect)

Note that the past perfect doesn't change. It remains past perfect.

- If the situation is still true, it isn't always necessary to go back a tense. Look:

  The earth goes round the sun.   *He said that the earth goes round the sun.*

  OR   *He said that the earth went round the sun.*

  My name's Isabelle.   *She said her name's Isabelle.*

  OR   *She said her name was Isabelle.*

  However, you will always be right if you go back a tense so if you're in doubt, change the present to the past.

- Change *can* to *could* and *will* to *would*. Change *may* to *might*.

  I can/can't hear you!   *He said he could/couldn't hear me.*

  I'll help you.   *She said she'd help me.*

  They won't tell you anything.   *He said they wouldn't tell me anything.*

  We may be late.   *They said they might be late.*

- You need to change the pronouns when you report speech.

  I'm hungry.   *The boy said he was hungry.*

  We can't find our cat.   *They said they couldn't find their cat.*

- Words like *today, tomorrow, next Saturday, next year*, etc. also change if the time period has changed.

  *We're going to the cinema **today**.* (said on Monday)

  *They said they were going to the cinema **that day**.* (said on Friday)

  *I'm leaving **tomorrow**.* (said on Saturday)

  *She said she was leaving **the following day**.* (said on Wednesday)

- People often make mistakes with the reporting verbs *say* and *tell*. Here are two rules to remember.

  Always put a personal direct object or someone's name after *tell*.

  Harry told me/Sally he was hungry.   NOT   *Harry told he was hungry.*

  Never put a personal direct object after *say*.

  Harry said he was happy.   NOT   *Harry said me he was happy.*

Word order

Test it ✅

1 Find the incorrect sentences.

a Think you that this house is nice?

b Why do you like John?

c Where lives Jim?

d I really don't know!

e Does Sam likes bones?

f How much does this postcard cost?

g I don't never go to the cinema.

h She likes not jazz.

2 Find the correct sentence in each pair.

a Lisa doesn't eat meat.
b Lisa eats meat not.

c I don't understand anything.
d I don't understand nothing.

e Sarah doesn't lives here.
f Sarah doesn't live here.

g What does 'oxymoron' mean?
h What means 'oxymoron'?

i Do you like this programme?
j Like you this programme?

k Where do live Alan, Mike and Pete?
l Where do Alan, Mike and Pete live?

14

GO to page 84 and check your answers.

Test it again ✅

① Write questions for these statements.

a   Jack works in Paris.

....

b   The sports I like are tennis and football.

....

c   Yes, David enjoys his job.

....

d   My old teacher and her husband live in Australia.

....

e   This jacket costs €79.

....

② Use these words to make questions or negatives.

a   the bus leave when does? ....

b   doesn't love me she any more ....

c   understands me nobody ....

d   how do often go you swimming? ....

e   does work in building this Mark? ....

③ Find and correct the mistakes in the newspaper and magazine headlines.

a
> *Pop star's sadness.* 'Nobody doesn't want my records,' she says.

b
> **WHY** does my child eats so much sugar?

c
> How much costs a new house?

d
> **BBC** staff like not their new boss.

e
> 'WHAT THINK YOU?' Opinion poll says 67% are against new government proposals.

15

83

🔧 Fix it

Answers to Test it

Check your answers. Wrong answer?
Read the right Fix it note to find out why.

1. a ~~Think you~~ Do you think → A
   b correct → B
   c ~~lives Jim?~~
     does Jim live? → B
   d correct → E
   e correct → C
   f correct → B
   g ~~don't never go~~
     never go → F
   h ~~likes not~~
     doesn't like → E

2. The correct sentences are:
   a → E   g → B
   c → F   i → A
   f → C   l → D

Now go to page 83. Test yourself again.

Answers to Test it again

1. a Where does Jack work?
   b What sports do you like?
   c Does David enjoy his job?
   d Where do your old teacher and
     her husband live?
   e How much does this jacket cost?

2. a When does the bus leave?
   b She doesn't love me any more.
   c Nobody understands me.
   d How often do you go swimming?
   e Does Mark work in this building?

3. a ~~doesn't want~~   wants
   b ~~eats~~   eat
   c ~~costs a new house~~
     does a new house cost
   d ~~like not~~   don't like
   e ~~think you~~   do you think

🔧 Fix it notes

A
Make present simple *yes/no* questions
with *do/does* (*not*) + subject + base
form of the verb.

B
Make present simple questions with
question words (*how, what, where,
why*, etc.) and *do/does* + subject + base
form of the verb.

C
In the third person singular of present
simple questions there is no *s* on the
verb. Use *does* or *doesn't* + base form
of the verb.

D
Don't change the word order even if
the subject of a question is long.

E
Make present simple negatives with
do/does not + base form of the verb.

F
Don't use two negatives in the same
sentence.

For more information, see the
Review page opposite. ▷

 Review

Word order

Statements

Statements begin with a subject and a verb:

Subject	Verb
I	*write.*

You can add objects, complements and adverbials:

Subject	Verb	Object
I	*write*	*books.*

Subject	Verb	Complement
Books	*are*	*useful.*

Subject	Verb	Adverbial
The book	*is*	*on the desk.*

Questions and negatives

- You make present simple *yes/no* questions with *do/does* (*not*) + subject + base form of the verb.
  Do you like eating out?   *Does he love Amanda?*
  Don't you want a drink?   *Doesn't she work for IBM?*

- You also make present simple questions with question words (*how, what, where, why, when*, etc.) and *do/does* + subject + base form of the verb.
  Where do you work?   *What do you think?*
  How much does it cost?   *When does the film start?*

- In the third person singular of present simple questions there is no *s* on the verb. You use *does* or *doesn't* + base form of the verb.
  Does he like coffee?   NOT   ~~Does he likes coffee?~~
  Does she want to go out?   NOT   ~~Does she wants to go out?~~
  Doesn't he go to school?   NOT   ~~Doesn't he goes to school?~~

- You don't change the word order even if the subject of a question is long.
  Where do Harry and Sally come from?
  How much do the computer, the printer and the scanner cost?

- You make present simple negatives with *do/does not* + base verb. Note that *not* is usually contracted (*don't, doesn't*).
  I don't understand.   NOT   ~~I understand not.~~
  She doesn't like flying.   NOT   ~~She likes not flying.~~

- You don't use two negatives in the same sentence.
  Fred never writes to me.   NOT   ~~Fred doesn't never write to me.~~
  Nobody cares about me.   NOT   ~~Nobody doesn't care about me.~~

Verb forms

Long forms	Short forms	Questions

Present forms of verbs

Present simple of *be*

Long forms	Short forms	Questions
I **am/am not**	I'm/I'm **not**	**Am** I?
you **are/are not**	you're/you **aren't**	**Are** you?
he **is/is not**	he's/he **isn't**	**Is** he?
she **is/is not**	she's/she **isn't**	**Is** she?
it **is/is not**	it's/it **isn't**	**Is** it?
we **are/are not**	we're/we **aren't**	**Are** we?
you **are/are not**	you're/you **aren't**	**Are** you?
they **are/are not**	they're/they **aren't**	**Are** they?

Present simple

Long forms	Short forms	Questions
I **work/do not work**	I **don't work**	**Do** I **work**?
you **work/do not work**	you **don't work**	**Do** you **work**?
he **works/does not work**	he **doesn't work**	**Does** he **work**?
she **works/does not work**	she **doesn't work**	**Does** she **work**?
it **works/does not work**	it **doesn't work**	**Does** it **work**?
we **work/do not work**	we **don't work**	**Do** we **work**?
you **work/do not work**	you **don't work**	**Do** you **work**?
they **work/do not work**	they **don't work**	**Do** they **work**?

Present continuous

Long forms	Short forms	Questions
I **am/am not working**	I'm/I'm **not working**	**Am** I **working**?
you **are/are not working**	you're/you **aren't working**	**Are** you **working**?
he **is/is not working**	he's/he **isn't working**	**Is** he **working**?
she **is/is not working**	she's/she **isn't working**	**Is** she **working**?
it **is/is not working**	it's/it **isn't working**	**Is** it **working**?
we **are/are not working**	we're/we **aren't working**	**Are** we **working**?
you **are/are not working**	you're/you **aren't working**	**Are** you **working**?
they **are/are not working**	they're/they **aren't working**	**Are** they **working**?

Past forms of verbs

Past simple of *be*

Long forms	Short forms	Questions
I **was/was not**	I **wasn't**	**Was** I?
you **were/were not**	you **weren't**	**Were** you?
he **was/was not**	he **wasn't**	**Was** he?
she **was/was not**	she **wasn't**	**Was** she?
it **was/was not**	it **wasn't**	**Was** it?
we **were/were not**	we **weren't**	**Were** we?
you **were/were not**	you **weren't**	**Were** you?
they **were/were not**	they **weren't**	**Were** they?

Long forms	Short forms	Questions
Past simple of regular verbs		
I **worked/did not work**	I **didn't work**	**Did** I **work**?
Past simple of irregular verbs		
I **went/did not go**	I **didn't go**	**Did** I **go**?
Past continuous		
I **was/was not working**	I **wasn't working**	**Was** I **working**?
you **were/were not working**	you **weren't working**	**Were** you **working**?
he **was/was not working**	he **wasn't working**	**Was** he **working**?
she **was/was not working**	she **wasn't working**	**Was** she **working**?
it **was/was not working**	it **wasn't working**	**Was** it **working**?
we **were/were not working**	we **weren't working**	**Were** we **working**?
you **were/were not working**	you **weren't working**	**Were** you **working**?
they **were/were not working**	they **weren't working**	**Were** they **working**?
Present perfect simple		
I **have/have not worked**	I**'ve**/I **haven't worked**	**Have** I **worked**?
you **have/have not worked**	you**'ve**/you **haven't worked**	**Have** you **worked**?
he **has/has not worked**	he**'s**/he **hasn't worked**	**Has** he **worked**?
she **has/has not worked**	she**'s**/she **hasn't worked**	**Has** she **worked**?
it **has/has not worked**	it**'s**/it **hasn't worked**	**Has** it **worked**?
we **have/have not worked**	we**'ve**/we **haven't worked**	**Have** we **worked**?
you **have/have not worked**	you**'ve**/you **haven't worked**	**Have** you **worked**?
they **have/have not worked**	they**'ve**/they **haven't worked**	**Have** they **worked**?
Past perfect simple		
I **had/had not seen**	I**'d**/I **hadn't seen**	**Had** I **seen**?
you **had/had not seen**	you**'d**/you **hadn't seen**	**Had** you **seen**?
he **had/had not seen**	he**'d**/he **hadn't seen**	**Had** he **seen**?
she **had/had not seen**	she**'d**/she **hadn't seen**	**Had** she **seen**?
it **had/had not seen**	it**'d**/it **hadn't seen**	**Had** it **seen**?
we **had/had not seen**	we**'d**/we **hadn't seen**	**Had** we **seen**?
you **had/had not seen**	you**'d**/you **hadn't seen**	**Had** you **seen**?
they **had/had not seen**	they**'d**/they **hadn't seen**	**Had** they **seen**?

Irregular verbs

Common irregular verbs

Base form	Past simple	Past participle	Base form	Past simple	Past participle
beat	beat	beaten	know	knew	known
become	became	become	learn	learnt	learnt
begin	began	begun	leave	left	left
bend	bent	bent	lend	lent	lent
bite	bit	bitten	light	lit	lit
bleed	bled	bled	lose	lost	lost
blow	blew	blown	make	made	made
break	broke	broken	meet	met	met
bring	brought	brought	pay	paid	paid
build	built	built	put	put	put
burn	burnt	burnt	read	read	read
burst	burst	burst	ride	rode	ridden
buy	bought	bought	ring	rang	rung
catch	caught	caught	run	ran	run
choose	chose	chosen	say	said	said
come	came	come	see	saw	seen
cost	cost	cost	sell	sold	sold
cut	cut	cut	send	sent	sent
deal	dealt	dealt	shake	shook	shaken
dig	dug	dug	shine	shone	shone
do	did	done	shoot	shot	shot
draw	drew	drawn	show	showed	shown
dream	dreamt	dreamt	shut	shut	shut
drink	drank	drunk	sing	sang	sung
drive	drove	driven	sink	sank	sunk
eat	ate	eaten	sit	sat	sat
fall	fell	fallen	sleep	slept	slept
feed	fed	fed	smell	smelt	smelt
feel	felt	felt	speak	spoke	spoken
fight	fought	fought	spell	spelt	spelt
find	found	found	spend	spent	spent
fly	flew	flown	spill	spilt	spilt
forget	forgot	forgotten	stand	stood	stood
forgive	forgave	forgiven	steal	stole	stolen
freeze	froze	frozen	stick	stuck	stuck
get	got	got	swim	swam	swum
give	gave	given	take	took	taken
go	went	gone/been	teach	taught	taught
grow	grew	grown	tear	tore	tore
have	had	had	tell	told	told
hear	heard	heard	think	thought	thought
hide	hid	hidden	throw	threw	thrown
hit	hit	hit	understand	understood	understood
hold	held	held	wear	wore	worn
hurt	hurt	hurt	win	won	won
keep	kept	kept	write	wrote	written